LORI PECKHAM, editor

BOOK CLUB

Guide's Greatest SPIRITUAL WARFARE STORIES

Nampa, Idaho | www.pacificpress.com

Cover design: Brandon Reese
Cover illustration: Marcus Mashburn
Interior design: Aaron Troia

The authors assume full responsibility for the accuracy of all facts and quotations as cited in this book.

Additional copies of this book are available for purchase by calling toll-free 1-800-765-6955 or by visiting http://www.adventistbookcenter.com.

ISBN 978-0-8163-6808-2

December 2021

Contents

Dedication

To two multitalented storytellers, writers, and editors, who have "finished the race" and "kept the faith" (2 Timothy 4:7). They now await Jesus' victorious return to wake them and take them—and all believers—to heaven:

Jerry D. Thomas: 1959–2019
Marvin Moore: 1937–2021

Also by Lori Peckham:

Guide's Greatest Animal Stories
Guide's Greatest Brave Believer Stories
Guide's Greatest Change of Heart Stories
Guide's Greatest Discovery Stories
Guide's Greatest Faith Stories
Guide's Greatest Friendship Stories
Guide's Greatest Funny Stories
Guide's Greatest Grace Stories
Guide's Greatest Hero Stories
Guide's Greatest Hope Stories
Guide's Greatest Mischief Stories
Guide's Greatest Mission Stories
Guide's Greatest Mystery Stories
Guide's Greatest Narrow Escape Stories
Guide's Greatest Rescue Stories
Guide's Greatest Second Coming Stories
"Insight" Presents More Unforgettable Stories
Jesus in My Shoes
Sixty Years of "Guide"

A special thanks to the authors we were unable to locate. If anyone can provide knowledge of an author's current mailing address, please relay this information to Lori Peckham, in care of Pacific Press® Publishing Association.

Acknowledgments

Special thanks to Laura Sámano, managing editor of *Guide*, for her invaluable help on this project and for her spiritual sensitivity. Don't miss her preface about this collection's important topic.

"Be alert and of sober mind. Your enemy the devil prowls around like a roaring lion looking for someone to devour. Resist him, standing firm in the faith, because you know that the family of believers throughout the world is undergoing the same kind of sufferings" (1 Peter 5:8, 9).

Preface

Dad was seven years old when my grandmother took him to visit Rosita—a young woman who would supposedly call on the spirit of a dead person. In a deep, loud voice, she told my dad and my grandmother about my grandfather, who had left them five years earlier. (My grandmother thought he might have died by that time.)

This scene is typical of the all-too-common practice of visiting spirit mediums, who claim to have communication with the dead. It is part of spiritualism, which will increase as we get closer to Jesus' second coming.

Let's get one thing straight. God's Word says, "The dead know nothing" (Ecclesiastes 9:5). The apostle Paul says that the dead in Christ will rise when Jesus comes (1 Thessalonians 4:16). Until Jesus returns, the dead are asleep.

So who spoke with my dad and grandmother?

Satan and his angels can disguise themselves to look like our deceased loved ones. Rosita was communicating with satanic forces—this was the direct work of evil angels.

When people "communicate with the dead," they place themselves in Satan's territory. This is a problem because Satan and his angels can pretend to speak on behalf of people who will be saved and also those who will not be saved. Demons don't value righteousness.

Sometimes spirits pretend to communicate on behalf of the apostles. This is particularly dangerous because Satan knows the Bible well and can twist its words to confuse people.

What's wrong with communicating with the dead if it's "fake" communication? What if you're just really curious?

Even "pretend" communication with departed spirits is of the devil. God specifically prohibited it (see Leviticus 19:31).

God has given us clear messages in the Bible. We need to know His Word so we can respond to Satan's lies the way Jesus did: with an "it is written" (Matthew 4:1–11).

We are in danger when we voluntarily yield our will to Satan. He cannot force us to do anything. Satan can win only if we allow him to do so. We can choose to be in a saving relationship with Jesus.

"I am no longer afraid," my dad says. "God is greater than Satan."

Whenever you're afraid of dark, supernatural forces, you can rely on the same God whom my dad and I trust. Remember that not even demons can separate you from God's love (Romans 8:35–39). "[Jesus] would sooner send every angel out of heaven to protect His people than leave one soul that trusts in Him to be overcome by Satan" (Ellen G. White, *The Great Controversy* [Mountain View, CA: Pacific Press®, 1911], 560).

Laura Sámano, managing editor of *Guide*

1

The Angels Lifted Their Car

by C. Mervyn Maxwell

Every foot the car moved forward seemed to bring the river another inch higher. Already water swirled dangerously near the engine, and some was leaking in through the doors. Everyone inside sat stiff and tense. If water entered the exhaust pipe, the engine would stall, and the car would have to be abandoned in the middle of the stream.

It all happened while Dad Larsen and his family were driving through the San Bernardino Mountains. Their Plymouth was pulling them quite faithfully, if not quite smoothly, over the rough mountain roads when it brought them to the brink of a rushing mountain stream. There was no bridge in sight. There was only a "ford," and the travelers were expected to drive through.

They stopped their car at the bank to survey the situation. The water was running fast and wide but apparently not too deep. At least, from the shore, it didn't seem too deep. Or at least to Dad Larsen's boy, it didn't seem too deep.

Dad, on the other hand, had a few misgivings. He

thought the river had more water in it than usual. Cars could cross it at certain times of the year, he knew, but perhaps there were times when they couldn't.

But his boy said, "It'll be all right. We can make it."

Even if the water is not too deep, he thought, *it is flowing mighty fast, which could make steering quite a problem, especially if the bottom is rough.*

But his boy said, "We can make it easy, Dad."

What about that waterfall a few feet downriver from the ford? It was hardly more than a cataract, but if the river current should force the car down to it, it would surely be enough to turn the car over on its side. Then the river would pour into it and ruin it.

But his boy said, "Dad, don't worry so."

Yet suppose the water were just deep enough that it came up to the exhaust pipe and stalled the engine?

"Oh, Dad," said his son, "let's go!"

Only Dad Larsen sensed how dangerous it really was. But perhaps because he simply had to go on with the trip or perhaps because he wasn't quite sure or perhaps because his boy talked so much, Dad finally said, "All right, Son, we'll try it."

His boy climbed onto the hood to act as pilot. Dad took his place in the driver's seat. The engine was started, and slowly, cautiously, the front wheels inched into the water. They were on their way.

And now the car was fully in the ford, and the ford of the river tugged at the wheels, doing its best to turn them down to the waterfall. They hit rocks the water had laid down, and the steering wheel spun wildly in the driver's hands.

The engine was in low gear, with the clutch only partly engaged. The car shook and roared. The family shouted their alarms.

"Hey, be careful! Don't try to go so fast."

"I don't believe we ought to have tried it. Why don't we turn around and go back?"

But from out on the hood came a voice: "Oh, don't worry so. We'll soon be across."

How could they keep from worrying when every foot the car moved forward seemed to bring the river another inch higher? Already water swirled dangerously near the engine, and some leaked in through the doors. Would the water run down the exhaust pipe? Would the car stall out here in the middle of the river?

They were not left long in doubt. All at once the exhaust burbled out the back like a motorboat, the engine choked and spluttered, and silence settled down over the stream.

All that broke the stillness was the steady rush of water as it swept past the wheels and over the nearby falls. And even now, the car was moving, bit by bit, down toward the waterfall.

What could be done? Dad pushed the starter pedal, but of course, that did no good. They were alone, away out in the mountains. The nearest tow truck was hours away, and the chances of another car coming in time were too remote to be considered.

The only solution was to lift the back of the car and hold it above the water until they could get across—but who could do a thing like that? The river was too wide, the water was too deep, and the car was too heavy. It was quite out of the question.

But it was the only way out.

And something had to be done fast, before the river forced the car over the falls.

And so Dad Larsen did what every one of you would have done. He asked God for help. "O Lord," he prayed,

"You can do anything. Please help us now."

And then a wonderful thing happened. It is almost unbelievable, but I know it is quite true. Dad Larsen told me the story himself and answered my questions about it.

Immediately, right then, just as soon as he had prayed, the family felt a strange, mysterious motion at the back of the car. It began to lift up, up, up until the exhaust pipe cleared the water!

There were three people in the car and one on the hood when it happened, and they all felt it. The boy didn't even know his dad had prayed, but he knew when the answer came. The car wasn't lifted clean out of the river. The rear wheels were left on the ground to make traction, and the springs were stretched so the exhaust pipe could clear.

Even more than that, before they could get the engine started, the car began to move forward by itself, as if hastened onward by an unseen hand!

Once more Dad tried the starter, and this time, with many a sputter and a gurgle, the engine came alive. He slipped it wonderingly into gear and added its power to that of the helpers from above.

The river current still wrestled with the wheels just as furiously, the river bottom was still just as rough, and the water whirling past the wheels was just as deep (or deeper) as it had been before, but now the car kept moving till at last it reached the other shore.

What a time of rejoicing they had when they were safe again! How grateful they were for the helpfulness of the angels! But the best part of the story as far as that family is concerned is this: That son had never wanted to believe in God. But from that day forward, he began to realize that there is a God in heaven who answers His faithful children's prayers.

2

The Monkey God Failed

by Kelsey Van Kipp

Nona Lakshmi lay sick with a high fever. She stayed on a pile of filthy rags in one corner of the dirty hut that was her home on the island of Sri Lanka in the Indian Ocean.

Grandmother had brewed medicine from the bark of the blue gum tree, but it didn't make the little sufferer feel any better. The old woman had gathered leeches from the grass that grew thickly in the stagnant water in the evil-smelling drains beside the hut. She had let the leeches suck blood from the little girl's body, but still the child felt no better.

Smoke from an open fire lingered in the straw-thatched hut, for there was no chimney, only a hole in the center of the roof. Across the floor, Nona could see her grandmother throwing herself down before a little brass monkey god. It was tied to one of the poles that held up the roof. In front of the monkey god sat a saucer of *ghee* (melted butter) as an offering. Beside it was a small pot of coconut oil with a lighted wick.

Nona trembled and shook with chills when her father

came in with the cow and goats. It was time for his evening meal of rice and curry, for darkness had come with its usual suddenness. In their eagerness to find food, the rats ran over the little girl's body. Grandmother threw some food outdoors for them, for she believed that feeding the rats would ward off the plague.

Later in the evening, several neighbors and friends dropped in to help Grandmother do *puja* (prayers) to the gods for Nona. One woman brought a Ganesha, a good-luck god, made of mud that she had bought in the marketplace that day. It had a man's body and an elephant's head as well as four arms and very short legs tucked around a fat stomach. Grandmother placed it on a block of wood below the monkey god, and along the top, she scattered dried peas and rice. Then the women and children knelt with their faces to the ground while a man called on the gods to hear and take away the evil spirits from the home.

Little Nona tossed and moaned the night through. When the sun came up, she was so weak she could not even lift her hand. Grandmother went to the store to get something tempting for her to eat, but Nona could not swallow even milk. The fever was burning up her body.

Grandmother was frantic. She had tried all the things she knew, but none had helped. The monkey god had failed. There remained only one desperate chance.

At the store, someone had told her of a foreign doctor in Ambalangoda village six miles away who had powerful medicine. The old woman decided that Nona must be carried to him. She had no money to pay for moving her granddaughter, but she must find a way.

That's how it happened that just after sunset the same day, a little old woman pushing a wooden-wheeled cart very much like a wheelbarrow came to the mission dispensary. In that wheelbarrow lay tiny Nona Lakshmi, very near death.

The doctor was kind, but he feared it was too late for his medicine to take effect. The beds were all filled at the dispensary, but to start back home so late was out of the question. So the doctor gave Nona some medicine anyway, and the old woman slept on the cement porch beside the rude cart in which the tiny sufferer lay.

With the dawn and the bustle of the new day, Grandmother rose to peer into the cart. Nona opened her brown eyes.

"Please, a drink, Grandmother," she said.

Grandmother was overjoyed. She ran for a gourd of water at the well. A little later, when the doctor came out to see his small patient, he found her much better and the fever going down.

Grandmother dropped to her knees at his feet, saying, "Your God is more powerful than our gods."

"That is so," he answered, "because our God is a God of love."

Reaching down to take one of her calloused, bony hands, he helped the old woman to her feet. He glanced down at the cart and thought of the long, weary miles she had pushed the wheelbarrow.

"You can understand love," he said kindly. "It was only love that saved your little granddaughter's life. Our God loves you even more than you love Nona."

The doctor could see that she understood what he was trying to tell her by the childlike expression of wonder on her wrinkled face. The old woman stood for a moment looking after the doctor when he had gone. Through her mind came a procession of the gods she knew: Shiva, the dancer with a bad reputation; Ganesha, the huntsman's son whose beard was cut off and replaced with the beard of an elephant; the devil spirits, which might come in an open door if a careless mother had not drawn a magic charm on the ground before the opening; Kali, like little children; the Juggernaut Car, under whose wheels many babies had died.

A God of love–what a wonderful thing it would be to have this God for her very own. Now her determination focused on finding out more about this God who was not only stronger but kinder than those she had known. She was ready to meet the true God.

3

Stuck-Up Stacy

by Bonnie Moyers

If anyone had told Stacy Steffey that she was stuck up, she would have hotly denied the accusation. *She* certainly didn't consider herself a snob. What seemed snobbishness to the students who knew her, Stacy simply called "discriminating good taste."

She was pretty, brunette, and very stylish. Her clothes were always in the latest fashion. Her room was lavishly furnished, and she had plenty of spending money. Her friends were all chosen from the "upper crust" of society—the "in crowd" at Valleyview Academy. Anyone who wasn't so fortunate as she was rudely given the brush-off.

Stacy enjoyed her tight little world. She was like the hub of the wheel, surrounded by her exclusive circle of friends. But her smug little rim was soon to be shattered.

The "shattering" began the day she first met Ann Baxter, a petite, lively junior with a ready smile.

"How are you, Stacy?" Ann greeted her one chilly

morning when they very nearly collided in their hurry to get to typing class on time.

Stacy stared at Ann in surprise. She didn't reply. She was looking Ann over carefully, trying to size her up.

The next day when Ann spoke to her, Stacy turned up her little snub nose as high as it would go and walked away.

"Wonder what's with her? Did I do or say something that would offend her?" Ann mused, half to herself and half to Cindy Barker, her chapel seatmate.

"You haven't done anything, I'm sure," said Cindy. "She's so exclusive, that's all. You'd think she was a princess or something. It's beneath her majesty's dignity to have anything to do with us commoners. But don't let the way she acts upset you."

"Oh, she doesn't really bother *me*," Ann countered, "but I feel sorry for others who may be more easily hurt than I am. And I also think Stacy is missing out on a lot of fun by not making more friends."

Stacy, however, continued to act as always.

"Stacy," Ann asked her one day, "what's the matter? Why is it that every time I try to be friendly with you, you turn up your nose and walk away? I'd really like to know."

"I should think," sniffed Stacy, "that you would already know! If you would only get with it, you could be a real popular girl."

"And how do I go about getting with it?" Ann asked.

"Well, for a start, get yourself some new clothes. Your skirts are *much* too long! And you could change your hairstyle. Your hair looks so childish."

Ann swallowed hard. She could shorten her skirts, she knew, but she could not afford to buy new ones. Nor could she spare any money just then to get the supplies the new hairstyles required.

"It's not really fair," she protested, "to judge a person by her clothes. A person could have a very good character, even if she doesn't dress in style."

Stacy regarded her curiously. "I don't read you." Her voice was pure ice.

No, Ann thought, *you certainly don't read me.*

Life went on as usual until the girls' dean announced in evening chapel that it was time to elect new girls' club officers. The president, vice president, secretary, treasurer, pastor, and sergeant at arms were elected.

Then Dean Rutgers said, "Girls, there is one very special position left to fill—that of girls' club pianist. To choose this officer, I suggest we have a number of our girls who can play the piano take turns. After listening to them, you can better decide who is best qualified for the job and vote accordingly."

Almost a dozen girls were suggested, and they went up and played one after another. Then Cindy suggested that Ann be given a chance. As soon as Ann had finished, Sandy Barr, the new president, rose to her feet and moved that nominations for pianist be closed. The motion was accepted.

The dean said, "And now we will call out each name and vote—"

But Pat, one of the new officers, interrupted. "Mrs. Rutgers, why don't we skip all this formality and have a show of hands for Ann? Everyone will agree, I'm sure, that she's the one for the job. She plays so beautifully."

"Are you willing to accept Pat's suggestion?" Mrs. Rutgers asked.

"Yes!" more than 150 girls chorused in unison. "We want Ann!"

Ann was thrilled beyond words and determined not to let her newfound popularity go to her head.

Her happiest moment came later. Stacy approached her almost shyly and stammered, "Ann, I owe you some apologies. I really had you down wrong! You are right—you can't always judge a person by his or her outward appearance. You are talented, and besides that, you are really very nice. Please forgive my rudeness. And, ah, well . . ." She hesitated; her face flushing. "Maybe I've made a mistake in judging some of the other students on campus too. If you'll have me, I'd like to be your friend."

"You are forgiven," Ann assured her.

Stacy became one of Ann's most loyal friends, and after all, she turned out to be a very likable person. Everyone noticed the change. It wasn't easy for Stacy to alter her long-standing habits, but she finally lost her reputation of being stuck up and stuck on herself. It was a loss she has never regretted.

4

Beaten Boxer

by Myrtle Fitzgerald

Almost reverently Niporn placed the flowers on the altar. Three times he saluted, palms together in prayer, and bowed to the ground, his forehead pressed against the dirt.

"Mighty spirits that dwell in the tree," he prayed, "I want so much to win this coming fight. I have fought eleven times and won each time. But this other guy has fought twenty times and has never been beaten. He's older than I am and as big as a gorilla. He'll surely mash me like a custard apple if I don't get some help. If you will help me win, I'll bring you some fruit and a chicken."

Feeling like a schoolboy caught looking in the teacher's answer book, the short, muscular nineteen-year-old rose to his feet. *How could I have come to this?* he wondered, running his hand over his short-cropped black hair.

With some distaste, he looked about him. There was nothing special about the spirit tree except that it was bigger than the other trees, with a gnarled trunk and wide-spreading branches. Filtering through the leaves, the sunlight made lacy shadows on the bare earth where all the underbrush had been cleared away. Scattered over the ground around the rough stones that composed the altar were withered flowers, chicken feathers, and bleached bones—mute reminders of worshipers who had paid their vows in days gone by.

From a nearby teak tree, a pair of mynah birds seemed to sound out their disapproval of his activities. Farther off, a heavy body crashed through the jungle—perhaps an elephant searching for water near the Doi Suthep National Park in Thailand.

Suddenly, the boy's thoughts went back to the day when he had dropped out of church school. The big, blond missionary dentist had urged him not to, even though he was not a good student.

"You need an education to get anywhere these days, Niporn. God needs you to work for Him. What can you do if you drop out of school now? All you've got is fourth grade. You don't want to go back to the farm and raise cucumbers for five cents a bushel like your mother and stepfather, do you? It's all right for them. They are older, and it's hard to make a change. But you—you've got your life before you. Don't throw away the chance to get an education. Think how your mother and father would feel."

"They won't care," Niporn retorted. "My father left my mother years ago with three little children. He's had twelve different wives since then. And I never did get along with my stepfather. I hate him."

The missionary bypassed the last statement. "But your mother?"

"I'll make money so I can help her with the little ones. She has a hard time now. Anyway, my brother wants to be a minister. One minister in the family is enough. And don't mention the mission schoolteacher! After that dead cobra I put in her desk, she'll be glad to get rid of me. I'm fed up with studying and having no money and following rules."

"Rules are necessary sometimes," the missionary returned thoughtfully. "And you'll be the first to admit that you haven't followed them very carefully. I do wish you wouldn't leave school, and I know your teacher feels the same way, even if she did get disgusted with the pranks. You may find it hard to get a job where you can keep the Sabbath. Have you thought of that?"

"Yes, I have. I won't take a job where I've got to work on Sabbath. I still love God, and I'll come to church every Sabbath, but I want some freedom, some fun, now."

Niporn found a job in a factory with enough pay so he could help his mother and give offerings on Sabbath. At first, he attended church faithfully, but his friends at work gradually lured him into questionable amusements, and his interest in spiritual things waned. More and more often, he found excuses for not going to religious services.

Then a new interest engrossed him—watching the boxers at their exercises and practice fights. His way home from work led past their training area, and many evenings found him leaning on the fence, observing them closely. Fascinated by the strength, agility, and quick thinking of the men, he failed to see the brutality of the game.

One day as he was watching one of the fighters hitting a punching bag, he could not resist throwing a few jibes at him. "What's the matter, fella? Can't you hit harder than that? Careful now, or it'll come back and knock you flying."

The burly boxer's face flushed with anger. "Maybe you'd rather I practice on you, huh?"

Never one to refuse a challenge, Niporn answered promptly, "When do you want to start?"

The big fellow's reply was to walk over to the gate and open it. "Let me get you a pair of gloves, and then we'll see if you talk so big next time."

Quick to catch the excitement, the other trainees gathered around, forming a ring. For a fleeting second, Niporn wanted to back out, but he knew he could never walk past the place again if he did, so he set his teeth and faced his opponent.

Wham! Biff! Bam! Blows fell thick and hard and fast. To everyone's surprise, Niporn won.

The burly fighter fell to the ground. He got up, wiped his bleeding nose on his torn, sweaty T-shirt, and held out his hand. "You're some fighter, friend. How about coming in for some real practice?"

Soon Niporn spent more and more of his spare time doing the rigorous exercises and learning the tricks of the prizefighters.

One day the manager came up to him. "Somchai was supposed to fight with someone tomorrow night, but he broke a bone in his hand and can't. Will you take his place?"

"Who, me? I'm no boxer. I'm just playing around here for fun."

"Maybe you're doing it for fun, but you've really developed. This other guy isn't so much. I think you can beat him. There's a good bit of money in it for you if you accept."

Niporn thought of his religious training. He'd had a guilty conscience while boxing, but he'd consoled himself with the thought that it was just exercise and recreation. He hadn't meant it to come to a real fight, but the amount of money promised tempted him. *I can give some to the church and some to my mother,* he mused.

"OK, I'll do it," he agreed.

He won the boxing match easily. The applause from the crowds thrilled him, and when his conscience raised a disapproving head, he slapped it down and thought of the large offering he would be able to give next Sabbath. One fight led to another until he had won eleven and had never been defeated. Forgotten now were his religion, his conscience, his mother. He rejoiced in the applause of the crowds, the admiration of the girls, the envy of his new friends.

One day after he finished his exercise, the manager stopped him. "Niporn, we've got a great opportunity for you. This is just what we've been waiting for. Win this fight, and you've got it made. Prasert has challenged you. Here's the time to make a name for yourself and roll in the dough."

"P-P-Prasert? Isn't he the fellow who's fought twenty times and won every time? He's a big guy. I can't beat him. What's wrong with your head?"

"Now, Niporn, you just don't know how good you are. I've seen both of you fight, and I know you can fold him up like an accordion. You've got to do it. You'll lose face if you don't. People will say you're chicken."

"I *am* chicken. I'm scared to death of that guy. I've seen him fight too. He packs a wallop like an elephant's trunk. You think up a good excuse. I don't want him making mincemeat out of me."

"Tell you what you do, Niporn. You go up to the spirit tree and promise the spirits a gift if they help you. They'll make sure you win."

"Tell me another one! That sounds real good," Niporn scoffed.

"I mean it. It's true. I know. The spirits have done lots of things for me."

Niporn didn't believe in spirits, but he was far from God now, and anyway, he couldn't pray to Him about a prizefight. At the repeated urgings of the manager, he decided to give the spirits a try.

One of the reddish-brown roosters with the blue-black tail feathers that somehow gave off rainbow colors, a kilogram of the big purple mangosteens with green caps and juicy white centers, and a prickly durian should satisfy them. What matter if the durian smelled like rotten onions? The rich, golden meat was so delicious. All this would be a small price to pay for success.

With a start, Niporn looked at the sun. He had stayed longer at the spirit tree than he'd intended to. He would have to hurry to get down the steep mountain trail before dark. Lengthening shadows gave an eerie feeling to the place, and uneasiness washed over him as he thought of what he had done. Were there really spirits in the tree? Had he prayed to the devil? Resolutely he put the thoughts out of his mind and went back to town.

The fight a few days later was a hard one, but he was victorious. In the midst of his jubilation, he remembered his vow to bring the spirit tree more gifts. But the way up the mountain was long and hard. The sun was hot. Maybe the spirits hadn't really helped him. Anyway, tomorrow would be time enough. But the tomorrows came and went, and Niporn did not fulfill his vow.

* * * * *

Time passed, and one day Niporn's mother wearily straightened her aching back. She pushed her hair away from her perspiring face, leaving a smudge of red soil on her forehead.

Someone was coming in a hurry. Something must be wrong. Dropping her hoe among the sweet potato plants, she ran to meet the stranger.

"Something terrible has happened to your son," the man blurted out. "The spirits have gone into him and are tormenting him. They will not let him eat or sleep."

"The spirits? Why should the spirits harm my son?" Mother questioned. "He is a Christian. Our God is stronger than the spirits."

"Listen, I am Niporn's friend Precha. I know that Niporn promised a gift to the spirit tree way up on the mountain. He didn't go back with the gift. The spirits are angry. They shout and curse. No one can get near Niporn. He threw Soonthron down the stairs and Nopadon out the window. Six men held him down when the doctor came to see him, and he broke away and beat up the doctor. You must call the witch doctor to drive these spirits out."

"Niporn promised a gift to the spirit tree? How could he have forgotten our Jesus! I must do something to help him, but what? I will not go to the witch doctor. I don't want him to look at Niporn through his little black box and see the spirits sitting on his shoulder like monkeys or owls. I'll go to see our Bible instructor. She taught us about Jesus. She will pray, and God will drive the spirits away."

Hurriedly preparing herself for the trip, Niporn's mother left her little children in the care of a neighbor and went to town with Precha. Peeping at Niporn through a window, she could hardly believe her eyes. Was this tattered, unwashed man her handsome, well-dressed son who had so proudly brought her some money a few months ago? Why, he was so skinny he looked like a skeleton! Surely it was the spirits that were glaring through his eyes!

Appalled by the change, Mother rushed to Miss Orapin, the tall Bible instructor with the neatly tailored clothes, and poured out the whole story; her wrinkled face working with emotion, and her work-worn hands creasing and uncreasing a fold in her black sarong as she talked.

"So you will pray for him, please, Miss Orapin?" she concluded. "It is only God that can help him now."

"Of course, I will." Miss Orapin slipped a comforting arm around the worried mother. "Our God is stronger than the spirits. He will cast them out."

Taking her Bible, she went with the distraught mother to Niporn's room. He was lying quietly on a faded mat, but when he saw his mother and the Bible instructor, he leaped to his feet in a terrible rage and rushed toward them. The two women sank to their knees, praying earnestly that God would protect them and drive the spirits out of the tormented youth.

Niporn could not come near them, but the spirits shrieked, "Why are you women meddling here? You can't do anything. Niporn belongs to us now. Your God is powerless. He will not help you." Then the weird voices cursed.

The church members were asked to fast and pray. Daily a small group visited the young man, read the Bible, and prayed. They searched their own hearts lest any sin keep God from hearing them. One day when the Spirit of God seemed very near, they suddenly heard a voice.

"Why are you praying?"

Opening their eyes, the people saw Niporn sitting up on his mat with a puzzled look on his thin face.

"Niporn, Niporn! You're healed! You're healed!" Laughing and crying, Mother clasped him in her arms.

Miss Orapin, a little more composed, told the mystified

young man what had happened. He could remember nothing of the eleven days the spirits had possessed him.

"I'll never have anything to do with the spirits again," he declared with a shudder. "From now on, I'm going to serve the Lord."

Once more they knelt and lifted their hearts in thanksgiving to the God who is stronger than the spirits.

Niporn did not return to boxing. After some weeks of rest at home, he went to Bangkok and found work in the mission hospital. He developed a talent for storytelling, and the story he liked most to tell was how he was saved by prayer.

5

Hope on a Bicycle

by Josephine Cunnington Edwards

Cindy Marlon glanced around the bedroom impatiently. It had been so pretty that morning, but now it was a great big mess.

She had cleaned it after Jenny, Patsy, and Louise had gone to wash up for breakfast. The beds had been smooth, and her little sisters' things had been laid out for them to hang up.

Now just look at it! Her powder was spilled where Patsy had dipped into it. Jenny had used her comb, and it was full of her soft, fluffy, yellow hair. A partly eaten piece of dried bread was on the arm of the chair, and the curtains had been shoved back. One curtain was draped over a picture. Little garments were strewn all over the room.

She had to pick up after her three little sisters all over again. "Mom ought to teach those kids something!" she said under her breath as she swiftly put things aright. "It doesn't even look like we're civilized."

She never could bear untidiness, and in a few minutes,

the room was in order again. She felt ashamed for her outburst, for Mother was trying hard to look after such a big family and was always working beyond her strength. Back in the 1930s, things were not easy, especially with eight school-age children.

Though Cindy and her brother Lee had work after school, it took money, money, money to buy clothes and food for such a "mob," as they called themselves. Father worked in the coal mine when there was work and came home after a ten-hour shift dead tired. They always had a large vegetable garden, which required a lot of work by everyone.

Cindy and Lee were aware of the hardships, but the younger ones acted as though a whole mint of money were at their disposal. The house was not very big—there were only three bedrooms, a large kitchen, and a living-dining room. Father and Mother's bedroom had baby Lily Jane's crib and the sewing machine, and the large back bedroom belonged to the boys. The big room upstairs belonged to the other four girls.

Mother's hair was faded and streaked with gray. Even with the fresh produce from the garden and eggs from their hens, life was a real struggle for her. She had to make Father's paycheck stretch and stretch. Someone was always out of shoes or mittens or was outgrowing patched pants or dresses.

Cindy helped all she could. She had a job at the soda fountain of Owl Drugstore, where she would hurry right after school and work until nine three nights a week. She worked all day Sunday and got off at five. She studied early and late and took pride in her grades. Lee had a job in the big Commercial Center Grocery chain. He kept coveralls in the storeroom and was hard at work fifteen minutes after school was out. No one could ever accuse either Lee or Cindy of being lazy. Cindy watched for fabric sales and made her own dresses at only a fraction of what they would have cost if she had bought them ready-made. And she could nearly always achieve a dainty little dress for Lily Jane from a length of lace and the scraps.

"I declare, I don't know what we'd do without our Lee and Cindy," Mother said many times, and Father, weary and silent, always agreed.

Lee could often be seen carrying home a broken sack of flour or a case of dented cans of food he had gotten at a low price. Sprouted potatoes or specked apples he could often get free, and such foods largely bulked out the family's low budget.

One thing about Lee: he never would give anyone a worry. He'd rather read than chase around, and he was so bashful that if he had so much as looked at a girl, everyone in town would have known it.

Mother was proud of him. She thought of him as deeply intellectual and hoped he'd really "be something" someday. "After all, my grandpa was a Baptist preacher, and Daddy's uncle was a doctor. No tellin' what might come of this, with his reading all the time," she'd say.

One day a book agent came riding down the Marlons' street on a bicycle. Lee had just come home from the store with a load of groceries. He stood just inside the door, listening to the sales talk; his dark eyes gleaming with interest as the young colporteur told about the book. The book, he explained, began with the terrible destruction of Jerusalem after Christ was crucified, when so many thousands of people perished in the siege, and it went right down through the ages, telling of the struggles of people who would rather die than deny truth.

"The end of the book is prophecy," the young agent said. "It is based on actual prophecies in the Bible that tell us what is going to come on the earth in the last days."

"I'm sure we'd enjoy that book," Mother said regretfully, "but we have such a big family that I don't see how we can afford it, much as we'd like to."

But even as she spoke, she caught a glimpse of Lee's face. It was so full of eagerness and desire. He had lugged home in the old store cart a bushel of specked apples and enough lettuce trimmings for several big salads, besides some for the hens. There were also some overripe bananas and several sprouted cabbages. He ought to have some reward for his loyalty and faithfulness. After all, what he had just brought home would make many meals.

"I'll take it," she said impulsively. "Our son Lee here is quite a reader. He'll enjoy it."

"You'll all enjoy *The Great Controversy*," the colporteur assured her as he went out the door toward his bike.

"Aw, Mom," Lee said, putting his arm awkwardly around his mother's neck, "you're just too good to us kids!"

"I'll find the money some way," she said, setting her mouth with determination. "Miss Liza is always wanting fresh eggs. I'll use the egg money for it."

It was that book that upset everything, Cindy reflected. From the minute it came on the place, Lee glued himself to it. The family conversation—almost all of it—took on a history tone until, if you didn't know history, you soon would or you'd seem totally dumb. Even little Jenny, Patsy, and Louise listened open-mouthed as Lee told stories of Huss and Jerome, of Martin Luther and the Huguenots.

Then Joe began to read it, and James, and there were always three bookmarks to look out for. Someone was always yelling, "Don't lose that shoestring! That's my place!" or "Hey, hey! That carton top is my bookmarker! Don't let it drop!"

"Of all things," Lee was goaded into saying good-naturedly one night, "Miss Postley at the library said she found a dried-up piece of fried egg for a bookmarker in a returned book last winter. Don't any of you try that shenanigan on my book!"

"Your book!" Joe and James hooted in concert. "Isn't it ours too?"

But it was Lee who delved into it the most. He brought home books from the library to read more about the subjects *The Great Controversy* discussed.

"I had Miss Postley get me some church history books from the state library," he announced one evening. "This Ellen White knew what she was talking about. It's all in the history books, only she makes it more interesting."

One evening he came home from the store triumphantly. "That book agent came in the store today," he announced. "I found out his name is Arthur Vernon. He's delivering books east of town and was hunting a place to stay. I told him he could stay at our house if he didn't mind sleepin' in my room. You don't care, do you, Mom?"

Mother was working at the stove, putting the finishing touches on supper. Patsy was setting the table, and Jenny came in with a pitcher of milk from the springhouse to fill the glasses.

"Of course, I don't mind," his mother replied pleasantly. "I hope you told him to come to supper. He seemed like such a nice person."

"Oh, I did," Lee replied. "I knew you wouldn't care, Mom. You're so good."

Mother shot a pleased glance at her tall son, stooping a little while he combed his curly black hair at the wavy mirror over the pump sink.

"We ought to put on a clean tablecloth," she began as Cindy came in, her eyes dark with weariness.

"Am I ever tired! Everyone in town wanted milkshakes and sandwiches the last hour! I think I'll be making them in my sleep tonight. Mind if I come to the table in my bathrobe?"

"We're having company for supper," Louise stated, washing Lily Jane's face and tying on her bib.

Mom was dishing up the fried potatoes as Arthur Vernon drove up in his rattly old bicycle. He got his battered suitcase out, and it seemed as if the whole family met him at the door and made him welcome. A clean towel and washcloth were given to him, and he washed in the basin in a corner of the kitchen at the old iron pump sink.

Then it seemed as if everyone ushered him to the table—and such a table! A golden loaf of corn bread steamed beside a pat of yellow homemade butter. The pitcher was full of creamy milk, and the big, tall glasses were full. A large dish of fried potatoes and onions, crispy and inviting, sat on one end of the table, and a dish of creamed lima beans was on the other. A huge platter of sliced tomatoes and cucumbers looked better to Arthur than the fried meat, which everyone else seemed to enjoy.

The young man was gracious and full of interesting conversation. They passed the pork to him several times, but he ate so hugely of the corn bread, beans, and potatoes that they didn't insist that he taste that good side pork, dipped in batter and fried so crisply, as only Mom could do.

"I'd like to ask you some questions about that chapter

in the book about the signs of Christ's coming," Lee said while they were eating some of Mother's good blackberry pie.

"I'd be glad to give you a whole study on Christ's second coming. It's one of my favorite subjects," Arthur answered, smiling.

He turned his glance toward Cindy, and she looked away annoyed. She hoped they wouldn't expect her to stay around. She and Bert were going to a barn dance at Pewee Lake after supper. She got up and started to help her mother clear the table.

"Don't do that, dear," Mother protested. "Aren't you going out with Bert tonight? You just run along."

"Yes," she answered. "He'll be after me in a half hour. But I'm almost too tired to go."

"Jenny and Patsy will do the dishes. I'll put things away. You just run along and get ready."

"Cindy," Lee called to her as she was halfway up the stairs, "I wish you wouldn't go tonight. Can't you call it off? I asked Mr. Vernon to explain things about the second coming of Jesus. It'll be worth more to you than an old dance at Pewee Lake with that numbskull Bert."

Cindy paused and looked down at Lee's earnest face. He was just about the best brother anywhere, and she loved him dearly. What other young man in all the world would help the folks and read and study as much as Lee? Bert Ransom, with his silly jokes and shifty eyes, was nothing in comparison.

"Please," Lee begged. "Please stay home with us–this once anyway."

"Oh, all right," she laughed. "You and my aching back win."

After dismissing Bert with a dozen lame excuses, she went upstairs and put on her pink dress and ran a comb through her hair. She came down to the first of what became an intensely interesting series of Bible studies.

Those studies changed the whole life of the family. Before the summer was half over, Lee joined Arthur in canvassing, and to his amazement and delight, he did so well that he got two scholarships!

"One for me and one for you," he said to Cindy.

So Cindy got ready to go to the college less than a hundred miles away, the one Arthur had told them about. Everything after that seemed to be a marvel to Mother and Father.

A buyer came and bought their place, and they moved to a small town where there was a church school. Father found steady work at a factory owned by a Sabbath keeper. Before another year, both Cindy and Lee were in the college south of them, doing well.

One day a letter from Cindy informed her family that her friendship with Arthur Vernon had ripened into love.

"I expected that," Father remarked quietly. "And I'm glad."

"We plan to be married in June right after graduation," the letter said. "Mother, I want a garden wedding. You know that rambler rose Father has been training in the corner of the backyard? I would like to be married right there. It will be full of roses in June. And listen, we'll be leaving soon after that. Arthur and I have a call to the mission field. I'm surely glad I took all that Spanish in high school and college. I'll need it where we're going."

Mother looked up at Father. Tears were streaming down his cheeks. But they were tears of joy, and she was smiling.

"Nothing like good children to gladden the heart, Mother," he said.

"I know it," she answered, smoothing back his hair affectionately. "But it was that book that started it. That book I thought we couldn't afford. That book Lee wanted so badly."

Father nodded his head. "You mark my word," he said slowly. "Lee will find his place in God's work too!"

And Lee did—he became a much-loved pastor whose church members always had good things to say about him.

"He studies all the time!"

"You can't stump him on any question in the Bible."

"We really have a dedicated preacher. And he has a sister in the mission field."

Cindy and Lee looked beyond their small horizon to "the high calling of God in Christ Jesus." And all because of a book and a literature evangelist and a mother who stretched the paycheck just a little further.

6

The Green Shirt

by Marvin Moore

Antonio clutched his briefcase tighter and stepped into the small grocery store. The smell of dried fish mingled with the odor of spices. He paused a moment just inside the door to let his eyes adjust to the dark interior. He noticed three or four men squatting along one wall. One of the men wore a green shirt. The owner of the store stood behind the counter. Everyone stopped talking when Antonio entered.

"Buenos dias, Señor Gonzales," Antonio said to the proprietor. "I have returned with your book." He set the briefcase down in front of the counter, removed a red volume with gilt edges, and handed it to the man with a smile.

The man frowned and took the book. He opened it and spent half a minute turning its pages, then looked back at Antonio. "How much must I pay you?" he asked.

Antonio took out his order pad and flipped through the pages of receipts he had written earlier in the summer. "You paid two pesos as an advance at the time you placed your order," he said, and he looked back at the man and smiled again. "That means there are only four pesos due today."

The man grunted, pulled open a drawer under the counter, and drew out a stack of bills. He spat on his fingers, counted out four pesos, and laid them one at a time in Antonio's hand.

Antonio reached into his pocket for his black purse. Opening it, he took out a roll of bills and added the four to it. Then he wrote another receipt. "Muchas gracias, Señor Gonzales," he said as he handed the yellow slip of paper to his customer. "I am sure God will bless you as you read your new book." He shook hands with Mr. Gonzales, picked up his briefcase, and walked out of the store.

Antonio thought he heard footsteps behind him. He turned around. The man in the green shirt who had been squatting along the back wall almost bumped into him. The stranger mumbled an apology and turned down the street.

Antonio called a cheerful greeting after him and started across the street. The sun, almost straight overhead, beat down on the pavement. Antonio stepped around a chuckhole. Half a dozen chickens pecking grain in front of the store on the other side clucked and scattered both ways as he approached. Antonio walked through the door of a building.

Ten minutes later, after making another delivery, he emerged from the store and blinked in the bright sunlight. Across the street, the man in the green shirt was still watching him. He felt the man's eyes on him as he walked down the street.

Antonio made another delivery, then bought two rolls and some guava jelly at a cafe and two ripe bananas from a street vendor. He returned to his room for lunch and a midday siesta.

"It is hot today!" Antonio exclaimed as he entered his

room. He took off his coat and tie, tossed them on a chair, and sat down on the edge of the bed to eat his lunch. Ten minutes later, he stretched out on the bed to rest.

Antonio planned to become a minister. For two years, he had studied at the Adventist seminary in the Latin American country where he lived. Shortly before the end of the past school year, the publishing secretaries of the union and several of the conferences had conducted a colporteur institute at the school, and he had volunteered to work. His uncle had offered him a job in his sawmill for the summer at a wage that would have covered two-thirds of the expenses for his education for the next school year. Antonio would have taken the job except for the strong appeal made by the union publishing secretary on the final Sabbath morning of the institute; he called for young people to dedicate themselves to the Lord's work the next summer.

His eyes still closed, Antonio smiled as he lay on the bed. *The Lord has been a better paymaster than my uncle,* he thought. *Already, I have delivered enough books for a full scholarship, and today's deliveries will finish paying for my suit.*

In order to appear fully representative of the Lord's work, Antonio had purchased a suit at the beginning of the summer, even though he had only half the money to cover the cost. Disappointed at his not coming to work in the mill, his uncle nevertheless had loaned him the other half of the money, with the understanding that it would be paid back by the end of the summer.

Antonio opened his eyes and looked at his watch. Stretching, he rose from the bed. He took the last dozen books from a box in the corner, dropped them into his briefcase, and put on his coat and tie. Then he knelt beside his bed. "Father, open the people's hearts to accept these books with Your truth," he prayed, "and put Your Spirit within my heart so my face will reflect the love of Jesus to each person I meet."

He picked up his briefcase. *If I work fast, without wasting any time, I ought to be able to finish my deliveries by sundown,* he said to himself as he snapped the door to his room shut and turned the key. *Then I can catch the bus back to the city in the morning.*

He walked through the patio to the front gate. Across the street stood the man in the green shirt. Again, Antonio felt the man's eyes on him as he walked down the street.

For about an hour, Antonio delivered books in town. By midafternoon, he was walking down a country road, delivering books to the homes of farmers and gardeners. He met a boy leading a team of oxen, and now and then, a horse and rider passed his way. There was also an occasional car. But for the most part, the road was empty in the hot afternoon sun.

Antonio found people in their homes, though. Always, he smiled and spoke cheerfully. Everyone invited him in to sit down and rest, some offering him a small cake or a glass of milk with cookies. And everyone took his books, even the people who had placed their orders without making any down payment. Twice, as he came onto the road from the farm homes, Antonio saw the man in the green shirt some distance down the road.

That's odd, he thought. *If he lives around here, why doesn't he go home and get to work?*

Hot as the afternoon sun had been, and tired as he felt, Antonio walked lightly as he turned down the road to make his last two deliveries of the summer. Even in the late afternoon, the cool shade of a row of trees growing on either side of the road felt good. A third mile beyond the trees,

Antonio saw his next house, and the last one less than half a mile beyond that.

The shadows of evening had begun to settle over the land by the time Antonio stepped onto the road from the last house. But he carried an empty briefcase. "Thank You, dear God," he prayed, "for the most wonderful summer of my life! I pray that I will meet many of these people in Your kingdom as a result of my work."

The road was deserted as Antonio approached the cover of trees on his way back into town. What had been welcome shade in the afternoon was a chilling darkness in the moments just before nightfall. Antonio quickened his step.

"Alto [halt]!" a voice from behind him ordered.

Antonio whirled. In the darkness, he made out the form of a man emerging from the trees at the side of the road. The man approached him cautiously, with his left hand in front of him. As he neared, Antonio saw that he held a pistol in his hand.

"I've been watching you these past few days," the man said. "You are carrying a large roll of pesos. I want that money." He held out his hand.

Antonio froze. *God, what shall I do?* he silently prayed. *Did You bless my work all summer, only to allow me to lose everything at the end?*

"The money!" the man ordered.

"But, sir, this is the money I need to attend school next year," Antonio said. "I'm training to be a minister for God."

"The money!" the man said, impatiently this time. "You give me that money, or you'll wish you had!" He stepped toward Antonio.

Antonio saw the man's finger move on the trigger. After

a pause, the man started to take another step, and his finger moved again. Antonio reached into his pocket and drew out his purse. The man held out his other hand, and Antonio gave him the purse.

"Now take off your clothes," the man said. "I can use that suit."

Everything! Antonio thought. *This man is going to strip me of everything I own!* But he stepped to the side of the road and took off his coat and pants, his shirt and tie, and his shoes.

As the noise of a car chugging slowly up the road a mile or so away sounded in the darkness, the man said, "Hand over that suit." His voice sounded tense. "I want this over with before that car arrives on the scene."

Antonio picked up his clothes and handed them to the man.

"Now you wait here, and I'll give you mine to wear," the man said. He disappeared into the brush under the trees.

Antonio heard a frenzied rustling of branches and leaves and an occasional hard stomp on the ground. Less than two minutes later, a pile of clothes landed on the side of the road. Antonio heard the crash of branches and leaves again as the man ran through the brush.

Antonio wept as he put on the old clothes the man had thrown at him. They reeked of sweat. The shirt hung on his shoulders like a sack. His feet seemed to rattle inside the shoes, and he had to hang onto the pants to keep them from dropping from his waist to his feet.

"God, O God," he cried. "I spent all summer working for You. Don't You want me to be a minister and win souls for You? How can I go to school and train for Your work with no money?"

Antonio picked up his empty briefcase. It felt heavier

than it had ever felt with the heaviest load of books. He walked a few steps toward town, then sank to his knees by the side of the road. As he knelt, he felt a bulge in one of the back pockets of the thief's pants.

"What on earth?" he muttered, and he reached into the pocket with his right hand. A moment later, he held in his hands a purse. For a few seconds, he stared at its outline in the dark. Then he tore it open and thrust his hand inside. His fingers grasped a roll of pesos.

Antonio's hands shook as he unrolled the bills. Holding them carefully in one hand so they wouldn't fall to the ground in the dark, Antonio flipped through the bills with his other hand. When he had finished counting, he realized that in his hands he held every peso he had earned that summer.

"Thank You, Jesus, for taking care of my money for school!" he said. "Forgive me for doubting." He stayed on his knees for several minutes.

Antonio fairly flew the two miles back into town. In his private devotions that evening, he again thanked God for protecting his scholarship money. "What if I did lose the suit!" he said. "That's cheap enough for a year's education."

Preparing for bed that evening, Antonio took a hanger from a rack on the wall that he had used on previous nights to hang up the suit. He draped the baggy brown pants on the cross wire and hung the shirt over the top. Then he stood back and looked at them.

"I think that's the most beautiful green shirt I ever saw in my whole life!" he exclaimed, and he turned out the light and jumped into bed.

7

Hold On

by Maylan Schurch

"Yucko," said Kirk under his breath.

"Yucko *what?*" asked Reid.

Both boys were bobbing in the water near the prow of Jack Kendall's new ski boat. Jack, Reid's uncle, was at the stern, emptying a gas can into the engine's tank.

"You weren't supposed to hear that," said Kirk.

"Yucko what?"

Kirk disappeared under the water for a moment, but when he came up again, Reid said again, "Yucko what?"

"Well." Kirk rolled his eyes. "This is such a great boat, and why does he have to . . ." His voice trailed off in embarrassment.

"Name it that?" pressed Reid.

"Well, yeah. Why call a perfectly good boat *Three Angels?*"

"Don't ask me," said Reid. "He got baptized last year. Maybe that's why."

Both boys stared up at the gold-edged blue lettering on the white prow. *Three Angels.*

The boat tipped toward them. "Got your skis on, guys?" asked Jack, peering over the side.

"Yeah," said Kirk.

"Something wrong?" Jack looked concerned. "You guys OK?"

"Oh, sure," Reid said.

"Then tell me what's wrong," said Jack.

"Nothing's wrong," said Kirk.

"But what?"

Reid tossed water out of his hair. "Uncle Jack, why did you name your boat *Three Angels?*"

Jack grinned. "Thank you very much," he said.

"For what?" Kirk asked.

"For noticing. It's working."

"What's working?" asked Reid.

But Jack just revved the engine, and the boat moved out from the dock. "Who's first?" he inquired. "Here, Kirk. Grab the towrope."

Kirk hastily gripped the bar with both hands and lifted his knees. "Hit it!" he shouted.

The engine roared, and Kirk was up in no time, slicing through the bubbles of the wake, "cutting" gingerly from side to side, holding on for dear life. Jack took him around the lake once, then swung him back to the dock.

"Whew," said Kirk weakly. "You didn't have to pull my arms out of their sockets."

Jack grinned. "That's only at half speed too. Just be glad I didn't let it out all the way. Your turn, Reid."

"What's working?" Reid looked confused.

"What do you mean—what's working?"

"We asked you why you call your boat *Three Angels*, and you said that something was working."

"Oh, that." Jack stared at them from over the edge of the boat. "The lettering on the side of the boat. It's working. It got you talking about it."

"But why did you call it that?"

"So I could get people talking about it."

Kirk disappeared below the surface of the water with a whispered "Yucko," but Reid said, "OK, but when people ask you about the name, what do you say? You can't sit down and give them a Bible study."

"I'll explain," said Jack. "Your turn. Grab hold. Tight. And I mean *tight*." He revved the engine, and soon Reid was skittering across the water. This time Jack made a wider circle, hugging the shore pretty closely before swinging out to open water.

"Did you see them?" he asked Reid when they were back at the dock.

Reid flexed his fingers. "Ouch. See what?"

"Hey," said Jack. "You've got to keep your eyes open. Those rocks just under the surface of the water. That buried log."

Reid's eyes grew wide. "Did you take me over rocks?"

"How come you're so surprised?"

"I trusted you. I thought–"

Jack smiled. "Of course, you trusted me. And I didn't betray your trust. I didn't take you over the rocks, just near them. We never came close enough to do any damage. You didn't see them at all?"

"No."

"And even if he did," said Kirk, who'd been listening, "you were going so fast he wouldn't have been able to dodge them anyway."

Jack nodded. "Exactly. I knew where they were, and I

steered clear. And since Reid hung on so faithfully—even though his wrists are aching—he came through safely."

Reid chewed on his lower lip. "Oh."

"Get the point?"

"What point?" asked Kirk.

"Boil the three angels' messages down to the bone, and here's what they say: first, put our trust in Jesus, the Driver of the boat; second, watch out for the dangerous rocks and logs of self-worship; and third, concentrate on gripping the towrope as hard as you can, because following the Driver is the only way to stay clear of these dangers. It won't be easy, but your Driver knows the way, and pretty soon He'll get you safely to the dock."

"And if I link up with another driver," said Reid, "he might not be so trustworthy."

"Right," said Jack. "Kirk, your turn."

8

Shot in the Dark

by Hurl Bates

As a police officer, I have to take all calls as serious matters. Any call can be a life-and-death situation, and many times it is. But not always. Like the call I received at four o'clock one morning several months ago. It all started the day before.

A group of "good ol' boys" had gotten together at the general store here in town. Now, as everyone knows, when a group of good ol' boys gets together, a lot of bragging goes on as well as the telling of tall tales. And that night each story being told got bigger than the one before.

By and by, the conversation came around to haunted houses, as it most assuredly will sooner or later when good ol' boys get to talking. On this particular occasion, the talk drifted to old Herman's place. This was a small farm about twenty miles up a dirt road, hidden away from almost everyone.

Old Herman had moved to town many years before, and the farm hadn't improved any in his absence. Herman said he'd give the farm to anyone who'd spend one night alone in his old house on the farm.

Well, Robert, one of the good ol' boys, told the rest that he wasn't afraid of anything or anyone. About this time, someone dared him to spend the night at old Herman's place.

Robert regretted it right away. But he'd made his brag, and if he backed out, he'd never be able to show his face around town again. So, under the circumstances, the only thing left for him to do was to spend the night at old Herman's place.

After several long minutes of discussion, it was decided that he would spend the remainder of that very night there. It was now approximately 9:00 P.M., and plans were made to drop him off.

The boys created their own little set of rules—one of them being that the only thing Robert would be allowed to take with him would be his pistol (just in case snakes or some other wild varmint should be in the old house). No flashlight. No radio. Just Robert and his weapon.

The drive out to old Herman's place was tedious; the long dirt road leading to the place hadn't been traveled on for some time. It had been washed out by heavy rains, with many places in the road having ruts and trenches that were at least three feet deep.

Finally, they got to the house and let Robert off for the night, with plans to pick him up around nine o'clock the following morning.

Now, deep down, Robert knew that he was a coward. After the truck had departed with his buddies, it was extremely dark, and ol' Robert was shaking in his boots. Walking into the house, he found a spot close to a window that he thought would be a good place to make a bed for the night. After taking his boots off, he made a pillow out of his jacket. Putting his weapon under the jacket, he lay down, hoping to go to sleep and wake up when daylight came.

But it didn't quite turn out that way. Robert had just drifted into dreamland when, sometime around one in the morning, he was suddenly awakened. Glancing around, he was sure somebody or something else was in the room. By this time, he was really shaking because of the whole ordeal. In fact, if ol' Robert had been through an earthquake, he wouldn't have been shaking any harder.

Looking down toward his feet, he saw what appeared to be two large white eyes looking back at him. Shaking badly, he reached under his jacket and pulled out his pistol. Aiming at one of the white eyes, he squeezed off a shot.

Like I said earlier, I received a call around four that morning to come to the local hospital. Arriving on the scene, I found Robert sitting in the emergency room with his right foot bandaged about halfway to his knee.

It seemed that after Robert had gone to sleep, the moon had come up. And as it had shone through the window, it had reflected off the toenails on Robert's two large toes. By firing at what he thought were eyes, Robert had managed to shoot one of his big toes completely off. (Still, if there is ever a foot race around here, I'm going to enter ol' Robert. He covered about eighteen miles to town on foot in record time!)

It's bad what happened to Robert. But then, whenever a person is deceived by some*thing* (even his own toes) or some*one*, that puts a person at risk. That's why it pays to follow a bit of Bible advice in *all* that you do: "Be as shrewd as snakes and as innocent as doves" (Matthew 10:16). Do that, and you'll improve your chances of knowing what's *really* going on. Don't, and you'll discover, like Robert did, that deceit can be a real pain.

9

Spying on the Water Witch

by Christina Dotson

"So who are you spying on?"

I jumped at the sound of my father's voice and toppled into the bush that I had been using for cover. Quickly, I pushed myself up, retrieving my binoculars and what little dignity I had left.

"I wasn't spying," I informed my father. "I was just watching our new neighbor; that's all."

"I don't know, Chrissy," Dad said. "Sounds like spying to me."

"But look at her!" I exclaimed. I pointed next door, across our wide stretch of yard, to where a partly built house stood on land that only a few months earlier had been a soybean field. "If that strange woman's going to be our neighbor, then I'm moving."

Dad followed my gaze until he saw what I was pointing at.

"Do you want the binoculars?" I asked.

"No, I don't want the binoculars!" Dad exclaimed. "This isn't a stakeout."

I shrugged and lifted the binoculars to my own eyes once more to get a better look at the woman who was pacing back and forth in the yard next door. The woman carried an odd-looking Y-shaped stick in front of her. She held the two forked ends of the stick in her hands and passed it along the ground as she walked.

"Who is she?" I asked. "And what's she doing?"

Dad gave a heavy sigh. It was the sort of sigh he usually reserved for my brothers and me when we tracked mud on the carpet or knocked over a lamp while playing indoor soccer.

"That woman is not one of our neighbors," Dad informed me solemnly. "She's a dowser. The Bermans must have hired her because they're having problems drilling a decent well."

Dad glanced down and saw the confused look on my face. "That woman is water witching," he said.

This time only the binoculars fell in the bush. "She's doing what?" I exclaimed. "Did you say water witching?"

Dad nodded. "Dowsers believe they have the power to sense substances that are buried underground, such as water or minerals or treasure. They use those forked rods to receive 'signals' from whatever they're looking for."

My mouth dropped as I stared at the woman next door. "But—but isn't that kind of wrong?" I asked. "I mean, only God has power like that."

Dad nodded again, then headed back into the house. I took one last look at the woman in our neighbors' yard, then followed Dad inside. I didn't feel much like spying anymore.

It took the entire summer, but the Bermans' house was finally completed. Not long after they moved in, Mr. Berman stopped by our house to chat with my father. After covering the usual boring topics of weather, politics, and tractors, Mr. Berman brought up the subject of wells.

Being the naturally curious person that I am (Dad would say nosy), I sat at the kitchen table, pretending to read, and listened in on their conversation.

"We've been having lots of trouble with our well," Mr. Berman complained. "We have to haul water in from town because we keep running out."

"A lot of our neighbors have the same problems," Dad told him. "Do you know the Wilsons up the road? They built their house around the same time we built ours, and they had to dig more than a dozen holes before they finally had a good well."

"It gets expensive, all that drilling," Mr. Berman said. "I finally hired a dowser to tell me where to dig. I don't usually believe in that sort of thing, but . . ." He trailed off, then shrugged and grinned at Dad. "So how does your well hold up?"

"Oh, just fine," Dad said casually. "It hasn't run dry on us yet."

Mr. Berman blinked. "Really?" he said. "You must have gotten lucky."

"In my opinion, luck has nothing to do with it," Dad replied. He smiled and leaned against the counter, and I knew he was about to tell the story of how we had gotten our well. I had heard it all before, and yet somehow, this time, the story seemed to take on a whole new meaning.

Our future home hadn't been much more than a skeleton of two-by-fours the day my father drove out to the construction site to meet with the men who were going to dig our well. Dad didn't know much about drilling, yet it was his job to tell the crew where to dig. So he set off across the weedy field that would someday be our backyard.

As Dad walked toward the men waiting with the huge

drilling truck, he sent up a silent prayer that God would guide him to just the right spot so our family would have a good supply of water for years to come. Then he took a look around our property and showed where he wanted the men to drill.

Dad had heard all about the trouble that other local landowners had been having when they tried to drill wells for new homes. Around here, people often wound up digging ten or twenty times before finding a good source of water. But on only the second attempt, when my father, relying on faith, instructed the crew to lower their drill into the earth, they tapped right into an underground spring.

"And you've never run out of water? Not once?" Mr. Berman was finding Dad's story hard to believe.

"Not once," Dad replied, and it suddenly occurred to me how amazing that was. While, all around us, our neighbors were running low on water just from everyday activities, such as laundry, my own family had never had that problem. We had been through summer droughts, huge water fights with the garden hose, and countless Sabbath mornings when all six family members took showers, yet our well had never run dry.

Eventually, Mr. Berman went home, still scratching his head and muttering about how some people had such good luck. Dad turned to me and smiled. I buried my face in my book and pretended I hadn't been listening.

"You don't fool me," Dad said. "You haven't turned a page in an hour."

I grinned sheepishly. I knew he didn't mind my eaves-dropping this time. He had told that story more for my benefit than for Mr. Berman's anyway.

"I guess God wasn't about to let His well be outdone by

the well of some dowser, huh?" I said.

"I guess not," Dad agreed. "See, it does pay to trust in God rather than in yourself or in some strange 'power.' God is the one who can work miracles, and as long as we trust in Him, everything will turn out *well*!"

I groaned at Dad's idea of a joke. Then I jumped up from the table and headed for the kitchen sink. I had a sudden urge for a glass of water.

10

Beware of the Lobos!

by Dorothy Rose

There was just one topic of conversation in the little mountain hamlet: *lobos*.

"The *lobos* are coming down from the mountains in packs."

"We all try to be inside after dark because of the *lobos*."

"Did you hear about the two policemen the *lobos* attacked last year?"

"I lost some cows to the *lobos* right here in the village."

"The *lobos*, . . . the *lobos* . . ."

So it went. In the bus, in the stores, at the bus stations, and on the streets, Pedrito heard little groups talking about the *lobos*—the Spanish word for wolves.

But Pedrito couldn't let that kind of talk frighten him. He was a literature evangelist whose work took him to all the mountain villages that cold, snowy winter. And it was because of the cold and snow in the mountains that the wolves were coming down from their highland hunting ground to look for easier prey near the villages.

One afternoon Pedrito arrived at a village in the foothills of the mountains. He asked if there was bus service to San Carlos, the next village a couple of miles away. When the ticket agent told him no, Pedrito decided he would just have to walk.

In Pedrito's country, the farmers lived in villages. They went out during the day to work their fields and then returned to their homes at night. Since there were no farmhouses between villages, the roads were lonely.

"I wouldn't want to be on the road between here and San Carlos after dark," a bystander remarked. "The *lobos* follow the valley right down that road and on to the fields."

"Yes," added another, "I always arrange my work so I'm off the road well before nightfall."

"I do too," said a cart driver. "I make it a point to finish my hauls early. My mules would make good eating for the *lobos*."

Pedrito found a cheap hotel for the night. He decided he would get up early in the morning, walk to San Carlos, try selling to its few business places and shops, and return before nightfall. With this in mind, he paid for his night's lodging and also for the next night's stay.

The next morning Pedrito left his suitcase in the room and took only a briefcase containing his books and a flashlight. When he reached San Carlos, he went from store to store, telling people about his health books. The afternoon passed quickly, and before Pedrito realized it, the sun had gone down behind the mountains.

What should I do? he thought. *Should I go back along the dangerous road at night? I do have my room paid for in the other village, and it's only a couple of miles back. If it gets too dark, I can use my flashlight. Surely the wolves don't come down in the early part of the night.*

Pedrito started out. The light still glowed behind the snowy mountains, and he thought of the text "I lift up my eyes to the hills . . ."

But night descended more quickly than he had expected, for the sky was cloudy. Soon the countryside was so dark that he could hardly see where he was going. Not only was the road muddy, but there were also puddles of water to avoid. Pedrito took out his flashlight and pushed the switch, but nothing happened. Apparently, the batteries had died when the flashlight had gotten slightly wet in a recent rainfall.

This was a shock, but Pedrito continued on his way as best as he could. The night seemed especially dark. Not even a star was shining.

Suddenly, all the stories Pedrito had heard about the *lobos* crowded into his mind. It was hard not to think of them. The previous winter two police officers had been guarding a lonely mountain crossroad when a pack of wolves had attacked them. The officers' bullets had done them no good.

And then there was the young man who had sat next to Pedrito on the bus. "I was only a quarter of a mile from the outskirts of town when I caught sight of a *lobo* looking down on me from a high bank above the road," he had said. "Then it disappeared. Thinking it had gone to call the rest of the pack, I began to run for my life in order to reach the village before they could surround me. Just at the turn that led into the village, I came face-to-face with the wolf standing in the middle of the road. When I stopped, it backed off. I shouted with all my might to my friends who lived in one of the nearest houses, 'Juan! Antonio! *Lobo!*' My friends came running out with their guns and began to shoot. The wolf fled. I never had such a fright in my life."

Pedrito resolutely pushed these thoughts from his mind and prayed silently as he stumbled along. He preferred to think of the time when a man had asked him, "Where is your companion?"

"My companion? What do you mean? I am traveling alone."

The man had insisted that he had seen a tall man in a white suit walking beside Pedrito.

"You may be right," Pedrito had finally replied. "God's children always have someone with them, though their companions are not always visible."

Remembering this experience, Pedrito took comfort knowing that he had an angel with him. He thought again of the psalm: "I lift up my eyes to the hills. . . . My help comes from the LORD." And he prayed, "Lord, now is when I need help. If only I could see enough so I wouldn't lose my way."

He looked up, and to his surprise, there was a little circle of light about fifty feet ahead. He turned around to see if a car was coming. No, there was nothing. It was as dark as pitch behind him and beside him. He glanced up to see if the moon was shining through, but the sky was as black as ink. Ahead, though, there was still that glow, just enough to follow the track and to show the puddles. Suddenly, Pedrito realized that the Lord was answering his prayer! A thrill ran up his spine, and taking heart, he pushed on.

Before long, he heard behind him the sound of an approaching cart and team. He hardly had time to think when the cart, pulled by a four-horse team, overtook him.

"Stop, señor!" Pedrito shouted. "May I ride with you?"

At once, the driver began to rein in his horses and stopped some twenty yards beyond. "Come on, get in!" he shouted.

Pedrito ran quickly and climbed into the wagon. At

once, the driver sent his team galloping off with the crack of his whip. Then he turned to look at Pedrito by the light of the dim lantern he carried.

"Who are you? How did you know my name?" he questioned.

"I don't know your name," said Pedrito.

"But I heard you call 'Señor Garcia.' If you hadn't called my name, I wouldn't have stopped."

Pedrito told Señor Garcia who he was, that he sold health books, that night had overtaken him on his way back to his hotel, and how thankful he was that the man had picked him up. The driver seemed to be convinced by Pedrito's friendliness.

"No, I wouldn't have stopped if I hadn't heard my name, not after what happened on this road recently," the driver told him. "I was going even faster right where you were because it seemed I could see better. I could even see your outline. I wonder why that was. But let me tell you why I don't stop for anyone." Then the teamster told the story—but this time it wasn't about wolves.

"There were two policemen driving a truck along this very road, guarding $100,000. Of course, they wouldn't normally stop to pick up anyone, but there were two priests asking for a ride. They were dressed in long black robes and flat hats. Since the policemen trusted religious men, they were willing to give them a lift."

The man was shouting so that Pedrito could hear above the noise of the cart. "Soon the real character of the men became apparent. They proved to be robbers posing as priests. They stopped the guards at gunpoint, took the money, and fled."

The rays of the lantern lit up the serious expression on

the man's face as he added, "The police have been looking for them ever since, but the *banditos* are still at large. You can understand now why I don't want to pick up strangers."

Pedrito could see that there was a double reason to shun that road at night.

Soon they arrived at the village where Pedrito had his room, and the driver stopped his horses in front of the hotel and let Pedrito off. With a friendly wave, the man drove on down the cobbled street to his own home.

Pedrito hurried to his room and knelt in thankfulness to the Lord for the two miracles he had experienced that night—first, that the Lord had sent him the glow of light, and second, that He had made the driver hear his own name.

Then Pedrito again repeated his favorite text:

> "I lift up my eyes to the hills.
> From whence does my help come?
> My help comes from the LORD,
> who made heaven and earth" (Psalm 121:1, 2, RSV).

11

Ghost Runner

by Derek C. Bowe

It happened one night as he trudged home from the movie theater.

Hesitating at the beginning of his street, Kerry looked at the signpost. It read "Burial Ground Corner." His neighborhood had once been a graveyard.

Darkness and quiet embraced the houses between him and his own home, making it seem far, far away. Fresh big-screen images of ghosts emerging from coffins and vampires biting terrified victims flooded his mind.

I was a fool to ever go to that movie! he scolded himself. *Now I'll have to pay. Tonight a ghost or vampire might catch me before I reach home.*

Suddenly, Kerry thought about Mrs. Rose, who had recently died. Long before he could reach the safety of his home, he'd have to pass her house. When alive, she'd been the picture of friendliness; kids loved the constant smile that lit up her face.

That doesn't fool me, Kerry thought. *Everybody knows people morph when they die!* The hulks of rusted cars littering Mrs. Rose's yard seemed to agree with him. He could almost see her crouched behind a car in her present state: gray hair streaming backward, eyes red and evil, her mouth revealing two fangs.

Kerry shuddered, planning his next move. *I'll wait here until someone else walks down the street*, he said to himself. *I'll let the other person walk a little ahead, and I'll follow without him knowing it.* That way, Kerry reasoned, he'd have the companionship of a living human being to help him pass the dreaded house. Soon he'd be safely sleeping with his Bible beneath his pillow.

He waited and waited and waited. But no one came. Meanwhile, the sky grew darker and darker, and the wind mourned through the trees.

"I've got to make a run for it," he cried aloud, trying to boost his confidence. "If I don't, Mrs. Rose will come and get me!"

In a flash, Kerry was off and approaching the dreaded house. *Lift those knees higher*, he coached himself, gritting his teeth. *Pump those arms!* As the house loomed nearer and nearer, he glanced to ensure that nothing would suddenly dart from behind a parked car.

But just then, Kerry seemed to feel an evil presence behind him.

"It's M-Mrs. Rose!" he sputtered. Closer and closer the presence seemed to come, until he could almost feel its chilly breath on his neck.

"*Nooo!*" Kerry cried, spurting beyond the clutches of the "thing." Houses, trees, garbage cans, fences, and swing sets passed in a blur as he increased the distance between himself and the ghostly presence. Faster, faster, and yet faster the boy's sneakers thumped on the street, bringing his safe haven closer.

The streetlight! The streetlight! Kerry panted. *If I can just reach it, the ghost will vanish!*

Straining every muscle, he burst through the darkness into the wonderful glow cast by the light attached to a utility pole. Immediately, he felt the mysterious presence leave him. Taking a deep breath, he slowed to a jog. Yet he glanced back every now and then just to be sure the departed Mrs. Rose didn't try any evil tricks.

Another few steps found Kerry breathing easier inside his bedroom. But even though he hid under the sheet and pillow, he left every light on. And he prayed that morning, in all its brilliance, would come soon!

"I figured I'd have outgrown it by now," Kerry whispered to himself ashamedly. After all, at thirteen, he felt practically grown up. So why was he still afraid of the dark?

Kerry thought back a few years to hot summer evenings when his mother sat on the porch, telling stories about her childhood. As he listened to her dreamy voice, Kerry felt transported back to those long-gone days. He could see children working in sugarcane fields, playing on sunny beaches bathed by gentle waves, and sitting up straight in hard-backed church pews. Kerry's eyes glistened with tears as his mother told how many of them had quit school to help their parents earn money. Even so, he wished he were a child back then.

But there was another side to his mother's storytelling sessions—she sometimes talked about ghosts. Those tales made Kerry's heart shudder and his hair rise. Strangely, at the same time, he really liked the spooky tales! He and his friends were never satisfied until their begging resulted in another spine-tingling tale about ghosts.

Going to bed after the ghost stories was another matter, however.

After each ghost story session, Kerry would sit sweating in bed. It seemed as though every muffled sound and passing shadow announced a ghost waiting to get him the moment he closed his eyes. When he couldn't bear the sounds and shadows any longer, he sank wearily into dreamland. But along the way, he shielded his entire body with the bedsheet and burrowed his head beneath the pillow.

Nowadays Kerry had made progress on his fears. He had stopped hiding under the sheet and had started putting a Bible beneath the pillow. Smiling broadly, he'd quickly fall asleep, sure that the Bible's power would ward off any ghost! Still, Kerry wondered if he'd ever outgrow his fear.

Kerry endured three more years of darkness, fear, and ghosts. Then, at last, something happened. He started reading the Bible instead of just keeping it beneath his pillow. But the verses in Revelation about spirits, hell, and many-headed beasts scared him so much that soon he placed it back beneath his pillow.

About that time, Kerry started visiting a church that met in a large tent. He found it odd that most of its members didn't eat meat. Even stranger was that they regarded Saturday instead of Sunday as a holy day. But something kept Kerry going back to the meetings night after night.

The teen was surprised that despite their unusual diet, the church members were surprisingly energetic and kind. Ushers darted up and down the aisles. In a snap, they seated visitors, handed out stationery and fans, awarded Bibles, and quieted babies. But it was the girls that the now sixteen-year-old boy liked most. *They're way cool,* he thought. He was especially captivated by their sweet personalities, although many of them were very pretty too!

With such great people surrounding him, Kerry accepted Jesus as his Savior when the preacher made his first altar call.

Then one night something happened that Kerry never forgot: the preacher talked about ghosts and the many-headed beasts of Revelation.

Throughout the sermon, Kerry responded mentally to the amazing facts attacking his long-held beliefs. He was relieved to learn that the beasts were only symbolic, representing nations and religious systems. However, he almost fell out of his folding chair when he heard the minister state, "There are no such things as ghosts!"

He can't be serious, Kerry thought.

"When you die, you're truly dead and can no longer take part in the affairs of life," the preacher continued. "But don't take my word for it. See what the Bible says about it in Ecclesiastes chapter 9, verses 5 and 6."

Kerry leafed through his Bible until he found the text. In wonder, he read aloud with the congregation, "For the living know that they shall die: but the dead know not any thing, neither have they any more a reward; for the memory of them is forgotten. Also their love, and their hatred, and their envy, is now perished; neither have they any more a portion for ever in any thing that is done under the sun" (KJV).

"Now the devil is a master of impersonation," the preacher continued. "Remember that in the Garden of Eden he made it sound as if a snake could talk. He did it so well that Eve fell for his deception and lost Paradise. Let's learn more from God's Word, the Bible."

In a daze, Kerry followed verse after verse, all of which led him to an undeniable fact: the dead can't come back as ghosts. What a relief!

The preacher went on to explain that Satan has been known to pretend to be a ghost. "However," he continued, "the person who receives Jesus as Savior has nothing to fear about fallen angels masquerading as dead people. As 1 John 4:4 explains: 'Ye are of God, little children, and have overcome them: because greater is he that is in you, than he that is in the world' " (KJV).

A light flashed in Kerry's brain when he heard these words, and he smiled broadly at their full meaning.

No more fear of the dark! he thought. *No more covering every inch of my body with a sheet! No more burying my head beneath a pillow!*

"What's more," he whispered, "no more putting the Bible under the pillow." Instead, he'd put it where it really belonged–in his mind.

12

Light to Defeat the Darkness

by Rachel Whitaker Cabose

A trace of winter's chill hung in the March air as carriages and wagons drove up to the small schoolhouse. The year was 1858 in Lovett's Grove, a quaint town in rural Ohio.

The people crowding into the building were dressed in black. Their somber faces reflected the occasion: the funeral of a young man who was dear to many of them.

Despite the sad event, there was an undercurrent of excitement in the room. A special speaker was to give the funeral sermon—James White, a well-known preacher from Michigan. James and his wife, Ellen, were visiting for the weekend, and many in the audience had come more to hear him than to pay their respects to the deceased man.

Only a few weeks before, there had been no believers in Lovett's Grove who kept Saturday as their day of worship. But an Adventist evangelist had been holding meetings in the schoolhouse, and forty people had accepted the Bible truth of the seventh-day Sabbath. It was an honor to receive a visit so soon from the movement's best-known leaders—James and Ellen White.

Boots scuffed against the rough board floor as people squeezed closer together in their seats. Some had to stand outside—the schoolhouse was full!

The low voices hushed when James stood to speak. He preached a moving sermon.

Then Ellen rose to her feet. "I feel urged by the Spirit to share my thoughts with you as well," she said. The crowd settled back in their seats, eager to hear what she had to say.

Ellen's face glowed with enthusiasm as she spoke of Jesus' second coming. "Those who have died believing in Jesus will be raised to life again. There will be no more death, no more sorrow and weeping such as we experience here today. What a wonderful hope we have as Christians!"

Suddenly, Ellen paused in her talk. "Glory to God!" she called out. "Glory to God!"

James stepped quickly toward his wife, who was gazing into the distance. "My wife is having a vision," he explained to the audience. "God often gives her special messages to encourage and guide His people, just as He spoke to the prophets in Bible times."

The people were surprised to see that while Ellen was in vision, she did not breathe, but she could still walk around. At times, she even spoke a few words, evidently reacting to the scenes she was seeing.

For two hours, the crowded schoolhouse was quiet as the people watched Ellen throughout her vision. The funeral was almost forgotten.

Finally, she began to breathe again and to notice the people around her. Realizing that the vision had ended, the family and close friends of the young man who had died left to take the casket to the cemetery. But many people stayed behind, hoping to hear what Ellen had seen in the vision.

They were not disappointed. God had given Ellen special counsels for the believers in Lovett's Grove. There were words of encouragement for some who had chosen to follow God's truth, even though their family had not. There were messages of instruction for those who needed to use their money to help God's work.

"But God showed me so much more than this," Ellen said. "He showed me the whole story of this world from beginning to end, starting with Satan's fall even before this earth was created. I saw God's plan for getting rid of sin forever. He wants us to know these things because we are living in the very end of time."

Ellen's listeners leaned forward, wanting to hear more. "I can't even begin to tell all the details right now," she said. "But God has told me that I should write down what I have seen so that everyone can read it."

The people filed out of the schoolhouse to return to their homes and farms, thoughtful as they looked back over the remarkable events of the day. What a privilege to hear God's messages especially for them!

Ellen smiled up at her husband as the carriage jounced along the road toward Fremont, Ohio. "Just think—in two days, we'll be home in Battle Creek," Ellen said. "I can't wait to see Henry, Edson, and Willie again!"

James patted his young wife's hand. "I know you miss our boys when we have to travel. Especially little Willie. But doing God's work requires us to sacrifice."

"I know," Ellen said. She gazed at the leafless trees along the road, remembering something from her vision the day before. "You will have to contend with the powers of darkness," the angel had told her. "Satan will make strong efforts to hinder you from writing out this message. But keep trusting in God. Angels will be with you in the conflict."

What new difficulties lie ahead for us? Ellen wondered.

The next morning James and Ellen eagerly boarded the train for Jackson, Michigan. As the train rocked and swayed through the countryside, Ellen and James pulled out their writing instruments and began to work. When they traveled, James usually had articles to complete for the *Advent Review and Sabbath Herald* magazine he published, and Ellen often wrote letters containing the counsels God had shown her in vision.

"As soon as we get home, I'm going to start writing about what I saw in the vision this weekend," Ellen spoke up. "The information is very important for the church. God has shown me some of it before, but this time I saw the whole picture so clearly. All through the ages God has been doing everything He can to save us, but Satan has been trying his best to turn us against God and bring us to eternal death along with him."

"Maybe you can write an article in an upcoming *Review*," James suggested.

"No, there's far too much material for that! I will need to write an entire book," Ellen said. "I'd like to call it *The Great Controversy Between Christ and His Angels and Satan and His Angels.* People must know about the battle for their loyalty that is going on behind the scenes."

"*Hmm,*" James mused, listening for a moment to the rhythmic clickety-clack of the train wheels. "That book title sounds a lot like the title of a book we read earlier this year."

"Yes, but that author had it all wrong!" Ellen exclaimed; her eyes sparkling with passion as she warmed to her subject.

"He called his book *The Great Controversy Between God and Man.* God is not fighting against us. He's on our side! This book will show that the real fight is between God and the forces of evil."

"And God will win in the end," James said with a smile.

"Of course! In fact, Jesus has already won the victory," Ellen replied. She settled her head against the seat back for a short rest.

When the train arrived in Jackson, Ellen and James hurried to the home of Dan and Abigail Palmer, glad for the chance to rest and visit with friends before continuing their trip. The Palmers had been some of the first Sabbath keeping Adventists in Michigan, and they were always happy to host the Whites in their home.

Soon Ellen and Abigail were carrying on a lively conversation. Ellen told of the meetings she and James had held in Ohio. "We had so many blessings on our trip!" she exclaimed. "In Lovett's Grove we met with forty new Sabbath keepers. And to think there were none in that town just a few weeks ago."

"Wonderful!" agreed Abigail. "How did the group grow so fast?"

Ellen opened her mouth to reply, but she couldn't say a word. Her tongue felt swollen and numb. A strange cold sensation struck her heart and then surged through her head and down her right side. She caught Abigail's look of surprise and concern, and then she fell unconscious against her chair.

"Dan! James! Come quickly! Something has happened to Ellen!" Abigail called.

The three gathered around Ellen's unconscious form. "We must pray for God to heal her," James said. As they earnestly pleaded with God to restore her to health, Ellen's eyes fluttered open.

"Ellen, how do you feel?" James asked anxiously. "Can you move your arms and legs?"

Ellen slowly wiggled her right hand and foot, but she couldn't move her left side at all.

"She's had strokes of paralysis like this before," James explained to the Palmers. "We can only pray that this one will go away as the others did."

Ellen feebly reached for her husband's hand. "James," she whispered hoarsely, "I don't know if I'm going to make it this time. Tell the children how much I love them."

"But Ellen," James protested, "you must hang on. We're less than fifty miles from home. God still has work for you to do. I'm sure of it."

They all bowed in prayer again. Soon Ellen's face brightened. "I can feel a prickling sensation in my left arm and leg. I can even move them a little. Praise God!"

The next morning Ellen felt strong enough to continue the trip. But when they reached home in Battle Creek, she was too exhausted to walk up the steps of their house. James tenderly carried her up the steep stairs to the second-floor bedroom.

For the next few weeks, Ellen felt weak and numb. When she tried to walk, she had trouble keeping her balance and sometimes fell to the floor. But her illness did not cloud her mind.

"I must start writing what I saw in the vision," she said one morning shortly after they had arrived home. She was barely strong enough to sit up. But there in the upstairs bedroom, pen in hand, she slowly and painfully wrote a few words at a time.

"The Lord has shown me that Satan was once an honored angel in heaven, next to Jesus Christ," she began. She laid down her pen to rest for a few minutes as the scenes from the vision played through her mind.

Ellen wrote about how Satan became jealous of Jesus and wanted to have the highest place in heaven. Finally, she finished one page. Exhausted, she lay back down in bed.

It took three days before she felt well enough to continue. But again she could write only one page. "At this rate I may never finish the book," she said to James.

But as she kept working, her strength increased, and eventually, she was back to full health. God showed her in vision that her attack of illness had been a direct attempt by Satan to take her life. But just as God had promised, angels had come to rescue her from the enemy's power.

By May, Ellen was well enough to speak at a meeting of four hundred believers in Battle Creek. There she told some of the things God had shown her in the vision.

Tears came to many eyes as she described the suffering and death of Jesus. "The angels could hardly bear to watch the horrible scene," she told her audience. "They wanted to rescue Jesus from those who were insulting and abusing Him. Jesus knew that the weakest angel in heaven could cause the whole multitude to fall powerless. But instead of asking God to deliver Him, He chose to go through with the plan for our salvation."

As always, Ellen's goal was to turn hearts toward the Savior.

Through the summer, Ellen wrote on, and God's Holy Spirit guided her as she worked. She told readers about great Christians, such as Martin Luther and William Miller, and the ways God had used them to point people to His truth.

She told readers about the deceptions Satan uses to distract people from following God. And then she looked ahead to the time when Jesus would come again to take His faithful followers home to heaven.

Ellen pictured again the beauty of the New Jerusalem, the throne of God, and the tree of life. She especially remembered the loving look on Jesus' face as He welcomed His people to their new home.

Finally, she had to lay down her pen in amazement. "O what love!" she exclaimed out loud. "What wondrous love! The most exalted language cannot describe the glory of heaven, nor the matchless depths of a Savior's love."

One evening in August, Ellen met James at the door when he came home from the *Review* office. "The book is finished," she announced happily. "And the ending is my favorite part."

"Let's hear it," James said. He sat down and closed his eyes as Ellen turned to the last page of her manuscript. The final paragraph described what she had seen of the new earth.

" 'God's entire universe was clean, and the great controversy was forever ended,' " Ellen began. " 'Everywhere we looked, everything the eye rested upon was beautiful and holy.' "

She read down to the end of the page. Then she looked up at her husband.

"We'll be with Jesus forever and ever," Ellen murmured. "And that's the best part of the whole story."

13

Strange Sleepover

by Joy Wendt

Joy searched the crowded gymnasium for April. She didn't have to wait long. Suddenly, she felt herself blindfolded by someone's hands.

"Uh, let me guess," she played along. "April?"

April laughed and excitedly blurted out the question Joy was expecting. "Well, what did your mom say? Can you go to the sleepover at Heather's?"

Just then Lori and Leigh bounded up; their springy red curls bouncing in unison. "Yeah, what did your mom say?" Lori asked; her mischievous brown eyes sparkling.

Joy felt a twinge of jealousy as Lori moved closer to April. She knew the twins would be perfectly happy without her in the group.

Now Heather joined the girls and echoed, "So, can you go?"

Heather is nice enough, Joy thought, *but the only reason she invited me to an activity of the "elite crowd" is because of April.*

Feeling like a mouse surrounded by a group of cats, Joy swallowed hard. "Yes, I can go," she asserted bravely, "as long as my mom can meet your parents tonight, Heather—I mean, your grandma and grandpa, since you live with them."

"That shouldn't be a problem. Let's find them!" April quickly responded, once again going out of her way to bridge the gap. Joy felt relieved.

Now, if only Mom will say yes once and for all, she thought as the girls hurried off to set up the meeting. She began to imagine the fun they'd have swimming in Heather's pool, playing with her cute dogs, or riding her horse. She could almost taste the luscious apple pie Heather's grandma would make, the kind she'd heard so much about from the others who had been to Heather's house before.

Thanks to the help of the other girls, the meeting of Joy's mom and Heather's grandparents turned out better than expected. By the end of the evening, they were talking as if they'd known each other for years. "I guess this one's a done deal, huh?" April laughed as she watched the adults visiting.

"Yes," Joy agreed. "I asked my mom, and she said I could go!"

"That's great! My mom said we can give you a ride to the sleepover and back home afterward," April added.

The morning of the great event dawned crisp and clear. Joy got up before anyone else. She was ready with bags packed and sleeping bag rolled hours before April and her mom arrived to pick her up.

When they reached Heather's home, her grandma greeted them and invited them to join the other girls, who were in the kitchen, munching on freshly made oatmeal cookies. After the delicious treat, the girls enjoyed exploring the place. The tour finally ended in Heather's bedroom, where everyone flopped on her huge pink down-filled comforter.

"This party is awesome, Heather!" Leigh gushed.

"Yeah, and your grandma really is a great cook," Joy added.

The girls chattered about school friends and other topics for almost an hour. Then Lori proclaimed in a nasally tone, "I'm bored!" She plopped down cross-legged on Heather's plush rug.

Leigh, always in agreement with her twin, added, "What can we do?"

Several ideas were tossed around, but none seemed to please Lori. Her discontent was fast spreading to Heather, and even Joy and April felt pressed to come up with something to make Lori happy.

Finally, with that sparkle in her eye that usually meant trouble, Lori exclaimed, "I know—how about a séance?"

"A what?" April asked in shock.

Even though April was not a Seventh-day Adventist, Joy knew she was a Christian. She prayed that April would think of something quick to change this idea around. But right away, Heather piped up, "Yeah! Let's see if we can raise up Elvis! My grandma loves him—won't she be surprised?"

Stunned, Joy looked around at each girl. Lori, Leigh, and Heather had already sprung into action, looking for a low table and something to use for a "crystal ball," as Lori called it. April sat speechless; her mouth hanging slightly open. Joy flashed her a pleading look that screamed, "Do something—they'll listen to you more than me!" But April stared blankly forward like someone in a coma.

Meanwhile, the still, small voice of conscience in Joy's mind grew louder and louder. Memory verses and stories from Sabbath School flew through her mind as though blasting from a loudspeaker. "The dead know not any thing."

"Regard not them that have familiar spirits." She remembered the story of Saul and the witch of Endor, with its sad results.

Finally, the voice in her mind firmly and decisively said, *You need to leave this room right now!*

As if in a dream, Joy heard herself say, "I'm sorry; I can't do this," as she got up to leave.

"What's wrong? Are you *afraaaid?*" Lori asked and then cackled out a high-pitched laugh that gave Joy goose bumps.

Without turning back, Joy quickly jogged down the stairs; tears burning in her eyes. Why hadn't April stood up when she needed her most? *So much for a best friend*, she thought as she used her cell phone to call home.

Mom was very understanding, even though Joy couldn't explain all the details on the phone. She felt a sense of peace knowing that her mom was on the way and that she had done the right thing—even if she wouldn't be part of the "in" group.

After hanging up the phone, she turned to find April right behind her, looking sheepish. "I guess I need to use your cell phone—somehow I don't feel well enough to stay the night."

"Must be a virus going around," Joy said, and both girls laughed with relief.

14

Satan on the Loose

by Shawn Boonstra

"Dad, can I talk to you for a minute?"

Kayla's dad slowly looked up from his desk, where he was poring over his usual stack of paperwork. He pulled his glasses down his nose a bit so he could look over them at his daughter, who was standing in the doorway with a laptop tucked under her arm.

"What is it, honey?"

That was Kayla's signal to enter her father's study. If he muttered or didn't look up, it meant he was too busy with his work to chat. If he pulled his glasses down, he was curious. She walked over next to his chair and opened the computer on his desk.

"It's this stuff on YouTube, Dad. I've been watching videos of the tsunami in Japan, and it's really starting to bother me. Why would God let something so horrible happen to all those people?"

This was a serious subject. Kayla's dad spun around in his chair to face her.

"It is pretty bad, isn't it?" he said.

"Dad, it's *horrible.* There was water rushing through the streets; it was washing away cars like they were toys, and it ripped apart buildings, and *so many* people died, and now the nuclear plant is leaking, and it looks as though dangerous radiation is going all over the planet—so *why* would God do something like this?"

Kayla, who had a habit of gushing her words until she ran out of breath, stopped to get some air. Her dad's forehead wrinkled as he looked at the tears beginning to spill out of her eyes.

"You know, Kayla, you've asked a very important question. In fact, some of the smartest people in history have asked the very same question and never really found an answer. Fortunately, I happen to know where we can find a good answer—but it's going to take a little bit of study. Would you like to see?"

"Yes, of course!"

He turned his chair back to his desk, opened the desk drawer, and pulled out a tattered little blue Bible that had obviously been well used.

"The smartest people in the world don't have an answer for your question," he said with a smile, "but God does. Have a look at this."

Dad opened his Bible to a page in the Old Testament, where Kayla could see all sorts of sticky notes on the pages, with her dad's scribbly handwriting all over them.

"There's a story in the Bible in which some really bad stuff happens to a really good man named Job," he explained. "In fact, he loses almost his whole family, and then he gets very sick—and of course, people were tempted to think that he must have done something pretty horrible to deserve it.

But God lets us take a peek behind the scenes of the universe so we can see what's really going on."

"You mean the *whole universe* is involved?" Kayla hadn't thought about that possibility, and it made her curious.

"Absolutely! The story tells us that God is holding a meeting somewhere in the universe when suddenly the devil shows up, claiming that planet Earth belongs to him."

"How could he say that?" Kayla asked, amazed. "He didn't create it! God did!"

"I know. But don't forget—more than anything else, the devil wants to be worshiped like God. That's why he started a rebellion in heaven, and when that didn't work, he started a rebellion here on planet Earth. When Adam and Eve listened to his lies and sinned, the devil claimed they no longer wanted a relationship with God, and he believes the planet now belongs to him."

Kayla thought about it for a minute. "So what happened to Job?" she asked.

"Here, let me show you." Her dad looked down at the Bible. "Remember, the devil claims to own the world, and here's what God says to him: 'Have you considered my servant Job? There is no one on earth like him; he is blameless and upright, a man who fears God and shuns evil' " (Job 1:8).

Kayla suddenly got excited. "Dad, it's as if God is telling the devil he doesn't own *everything*, isn't it? Job was proof that not everybody was following Satan!"

"That's right." Her dad was obviously impressed. "So Satan hatches a plan to change that. He tells God that Job worships Him only because God has allowed Job to become rich and successful. Here, listen to what he tells God: 'But now stretch out your hand and strike everything he has, and he will surely curse you to your face' " (verse 11).

"Dad, what exactly does that mean?"

"Honey, the devil is daring God to hurt Job—to take away his blessings. He's basically saying, 'Listen, God: people follow You only because of the stuff You give them, but if You take it away, they'll follow me like everybody else.' "

"Tell me God didn't do it!" The thought that God might take a dare from the devil really bothered Kayla.

"No, not at all—that's the best part of this story. Listen to God's answer—and listen very carefully:

> "The LORD said to Satan, 'Very well, then, everything he has is in your power, but on the man himself do not lay a finger.'
>
> "Then Satan went out from the presence of the LORD" (verse 12).

"Wait a minute!" Kayla said excitedly. "God didn't do it—Satan did. It's like God was saying, 'Satan, I know that Job is good, and I know you're lying, but you do whatever you're going to do and see what happens.' "

"That's right. It's not God who causes misery on this planet; it's the devil. Also, it's really important to notice the limits God places on what He allows the devil to do."

Kayla was happy with the answer. What a relief! It wasn't God bringing disasters on the planet; it was all because of Satan's rebellion. Kayla was just about to pick up the computer and leave again, but then she thought of something else.

"Dad, why would God let the devil do that stuff? And what's the devil's point, anyway? Doesn't it just make him look really bad?"

"You'd think so, wouldn't you?" Her dad's forehead wrinkled up again. "But let me ask you this: When you saw those videos on YouTube and all that suffering, who did you think was responsible at first?"

That was a good question, and Kayla was a little embarrassed to admit it: "I kind of blamed God, didn't I?"

"That's right. Most people do. Now think about it: If you were the devil—"

Kayla interrupted. "Dad, I don't think I'd *want* to be!"

"I know, but just think about it for a moment. If you were the devil, and you were trying to get people to turn against God, what would you do?"

Kayla paused, then said, "I'd do bad things to people and make them think God was doing it."

"Exactly. That's the devil's plan to turn us all against God. Satan wants us to think poorly of our heavenly Father. But if you read the Bible and get to know God personally, it doesn't take long to figure out that He's not like that. Not at all! I mean, why would God do bad things to people and then give His own Son's life to save them? It doesn't make sense, does it?"

"No, it doesn't. And the Bible says God is love—so it's obvious the bad stuff isn't coming from Him. But why does He let the devil do this stuff?"

Her dad leaned back in his chair and looked up at the ceiling. After a moment, he looked back down at Kayla and asked a question. "Well, what do *you* think about the mess the devil is making?"

"If that's what the devil is like, I think he can't be trusted."

Her dad smiled broadly. "You nailed it! That's exactly why God has allowed the devil to do what he wants for a little while. He knew that Satan would prove that rebellion against God leads to disaster and that people who thought about it would see that the devil is a murderer and that God is love."

Kayla smiled too. "And once we've seen how much pain the devil causes, we'll never choose to rebel against God again."

"That's right, honey. And God has a plan to stop the pain forever once people have had a chance to learn about His love and make their own decision."

Kayla suddenly grabbed the laptop. "People need to know this! I'm going to post something under the video so people can know what's actually going on and how much God loves them and that He's going to make things right and how they can choose Jesus and how the devil is trying to keep us away from Him, and–"

Kayla was gushing again, and she stopped to catch her breath. "And maybe my friends can help. Maybe if we all just started posting 'God didn't do this–God is love!' on all these kinds of videos, it might catch on."

Dad reached over and patted her arm. "That, my dear, is a fantastic idea."

This story was published in the *Guide* insert *Visionary*, First Quarter 2012, and is compliments of the Ellen G. White Estate.

15

The Book on the Bottom Shelf

by David Asscherick

"This book has been a tremendous blessing to me, and I think you'll like it too," Mary said sweetly yet matter-of-factly as she placed it in my hands.

I took the book, mainly out of politeness. Mary was a friend, after all, even if her religious views struck me as, well, a little weird! At the time, I was a twenty-three-year-old vegan punk rocker, complete with wild hair and tattoos. I had no idea how big an impact that book would have on the course of my life.

The book almost went in the trash that night. Instead, it ended up on the shelf, where it sat collecting dust for many months. Then something terrible happened. At least, it seemed terrible at the time. My longtime girlfriend broke up with me, sending me into an emotional nosedive. I was a wreck, and all my friends could see it. They worried about me, but I would just sit in my room moping.

Then it happened.

I remember it as if it were yesterday. I was sitting in

my room on a cold, wintry day in October. As a university student, I owned and read many books, and on this particular day, I was listlessly staring at my bookshelf. One book above all the others caught my attention. It was Mary's book. A struggle ensued in which I wrestled internally about whether or not to get up, walk across the room, and take the book from the shelf—the *bottom* shelf, of course.

And then, suddenly, I did it. I rose, walked over to the shelf, and took the book from its long-standing place of rest. As I stared intently at the cover, it occurred to me that I'd never even noticed the title before—*The Great Controversy*.

What an interesting title, I remember thinking.

I sat down and began to read.

That was fifteen years ago.

Today I've dedicated my life to teaching others what I've learned in those pages. By far, the most important thing I've learned isn't a "thing" at all. It's a who! And the *who* is Jesus Christ!

The opening scene in *The Great Controversy* finds Jesus crying over the city of Jerusalem because of the people's unbelief (Luke 19). As someone who'd spent many days in the previous several months crying, I could relate. Or at least, I thought I could. I was crying for myself, but Jesus was crying for others. I immediately thought, *Who is this Man? Why is He crying for others? Why do I feel drawn to Him?*

I met Jesus Christ in the pages of *The Great Controversy*. And that is exactly why Ellen White wrote the book more than 150 years ago!

The Great Controversy traces the conflict between Jesus and Satan throughout the church's history, right down to the victorious climax of the Second Coming. First published in 1858 as part of the *Spiritual Gifts* volumes, the book began with a vision Ellen White received in Lovett's Grove, Ohio, that same year. That first version was written primarily for the encouragement of several thousand Sabbath-keeping Adventists scattered across the eastern United States. Soon Adventists were sharing it enthusiastically with their friends and neighbors, just as Mary would share it with me more than a century later!

Ellen White, who continued to receive visions revealing the conflict between Jesus Christ and Satan, felt impressed that a version of *The Great Controversy* should be produced that could be sold door-to-door. When she traveled to Europe for two years beginning in 1885, she visited many of the places she had been shown in vision. This made the history come alive in a new and urgent way. She must write—and fast!

In 1888, the expanded book rolled off the press by the tens of thousands. Seventh-day Adventists began sharing the book widely, and as a result, many new members were baptized. No one was happier than Ellen White. Because of *The Great Controversy*, people, by the thousands, were coming to Jesus and His church.

So many books were printed that the printing plates wore out! By 1909, it became clear that new printing plates would need to be made. This gave Ellen White the opportunity to make a few additional changes to the book that made it easier to understand. In 1911, the project was complete, and the latest edition was soon rolling off the presses and into eager hands.

In 1858, when she received the vision at Lovett's Grove, Ellen White was thirty years old. In 1911, when she held the revised edition fresh in her hands, she was eighty-three. She had given her whole life to Jesus and to spreading the truth of the great war raging between Christ and His angels and Satan and his angels.

This war will soon come to an end! Jesus, the King of kings and Lord of lords, will be crowned triumphant.

I'm so glad someone shared this amazing book with me.

Why not read the book yourself, discover the future, and share it with a friend?

This story was published in the *Guide* insert *Visionary*, Fourth Quarter 2012, and is compliments of the Ellen G. White Estate.

16

The Spirit String

by Patti Emanuele

He sat at the table with Josh and his parents every night for meals. He was silent, and his eyes remained downcast during prayer. His hands were tightly clenched in his lap. Sovann knew how to wait for his meal.

He was a small boy, with straight brown hair, worn but clean clothes, and dusty sandals.

Until recently, Sovann had lived in a nearby village. Josh had found him crying by the side of the road near the mission compound; his hands covering his face while the hot Cambodian sun beat down upon his shoulders.

"Come home with me," Josh had invited. He knew that his family would help his new friend.

Josh learned that Sovann's parents lived nearby and had driven him away when he told them he wanted to follow Jesus. So Sovann ended up staying with Josh and his family. The boy was eager to help and scurried through his day as if unwilling to let unhappiness catch up with him.

Tonight, as always, Sovann quietly watched as others

spooned their food onto their plates.

"Your turn," Josh said. He held out a bowl of rice to his friend.

Sovann grinned and looked around. When he was convinced that others had taken plenty of food, he helped himself to a modest portion. A string around his wrist, once white, now gray, with a stone knotted into it banged against his plate.

"Why do you wear that string around your wrist all the time?" Josh asked.

"It has been on my wrist since I was a baby. It keeps the spirits happy. It is my spirit string," Sovann explained.

When the house was quiet and Sovann had gone to bed, Josh asked, "Dad, do you think Sovann will ever be able to return to his family?"

Lowering his voice, his father said, "I don't know. He told his family that he is a Christian now, and they made him leave his village. It has been very hard for him."

The next day Josh watched as Sovann played with their dog, teaching him to jump.

"Sovann hasn't cut his spirit string yet," Josh's mother observed.

"No, he hasn't," Dad said.

The following day Josh and Dad packed their car with supplies. The entire family visited the people in the surrounding villages regularly.

"Why are we bringing scissors along with our Bibles?" Josh asked his dad.

"Most Cambodian people wear spirit strings around their waists, wrists, or necks. They've worn them ever since they were little babies."

"But why?" asked Josh.

"Well, their parents paid a *Kru Khmer*, or witch doctor, to put these strings in place," Dad continued. "They tell the people that the strings will protect them from evil and bring prosperity, sort of like a good-luck charm. They wear these strings for their whole lives. They are afraid to remove them."

"But Sovann is a Christian. He knows the truth about that kind of stuff," Josh responded.

"When a new believer realizes that in order to totally follow Christ they must be willing to cut any attachment to the spirits they had formerly worshiped, it can be very hard, even traumatic," Dad replied.

In Cambodia, there were a lot of reasons people would claim to have become a Christian. Many people were poor or sick, and they would say they were Christians in order to receive certain medicines or food. What they didn't realize was that the missionaries would help them any way they could, even if they were not Christians.

Sovann also claimed to be a Christian. He would come to Bible readings, sit through prayers, and knew all the right words to say. Josh learned that his family was very poor. At the end of the Bible studies, food would be handed out to everyone who came. Sometimes it was the only food people had eaten for days.

Sovann's attendance encouraged Josh, and he said to his dad, "Sovann tells me he's a Christian." He nodded toward his friend, who had taken a seat as Josh brought out his Bible.

"That's great," his father said. "We're not here to judge anyone or 'make' them believe in Jesus," he reminded Josh. "We're here to be obedient to God by telling others about His Son and what He did for them. We can only tell them. Whether or not to truly follow Jesus is their decision."

Josh thought about this for a long time. It really took the pressure off. He wasn't responsible for his friend's salvation. In the end, it really was a personal choice. He would keep Sovann in his prayers.

"Many times once a spirit string is discovered to be cut, that person's life changes forever," Dad added. "The person can be banished from his family and have their wealth taken away, and sometimes the new believer may even be killed."

"Wow," Josh responded softly.

"Eventually, if Sovann really wants to follow Jesus, he will feel led to remove his spirit string. It will be his decision."

One day Josh, his father, and Sovann went to visit the people in a nearby village.

"Please come, and bring medicines!" a woman urged, pulling on Josh's arm.

They followed her to a small house. Inside, a woman lay on a pallet, moaning. "She is my auntie!" Sovann exclaimed.

The woman recognized Sovann. "You," she said with labored breath, "go away." She waved her hands.

Sovann stepped back as Josh's father, a doctor, examined the woman and gave her medicine. The woman began to get better. Sovann cared for her every day until she was well.

"Your father gave my auntie medicine," Sovann said to Josh one day. "She did not tell him that she was a Christian, yet he freely gave it to her."

"My dad gave her medicine because he cared that she would get better. It's what Jesus would do, and we care about your auntie just as Jesus would," Josh said.

Sovann nodded. He looked down at his spirit string and grasped it. "I want to cut my spirit string," he said.

Josh ran to their vehicle and pulled out a pair of scissors.

He grinned and cut the string around his friend's wrist.

When the string fell away, Sovann stared at his wrist. He rubbed the skin slowly with his other hand.

"Now I am truly free," he said with a smile.

From then on, Sovann urged his friends and family and all who would listen to cut their spirit string. Soon there were many who had removed their spirit strings and carried a pair of scissors with their Bibles as they traveled.

17

Conquering Nahak

by Ellen Weaver Bailey

It wasn't easy to love the cannibals of the New Hebrides (now Vanuatu). After all, the first two missionaries to reach the islands had been immediately clubbed to death, cooked, and eaten!

Some of the residents on the island of Tanna seemed to be friendly with missionary John Paton and the converts from Aneityum Island, who worked with him as teachers. Yet John could never completely trust the Tannese.

For one thing, they were ruled by fear—fear of other islanders and fear of the evil spirits they served. Their "sacred men," and a few "sacred women," were especially feared for their use of *nahak*, or magic spells, to injure and kill. Wars were frequent and could break out suddenly over old quarrels.

During one of these wars, John circulated among the people, trying to stop the killing. "War is evil. It does no good to anyone," he said. He pleaded with the chiefs, "Please stop the war!"

At this point, three chiefs, who were also sacred men, or sorcerers, decided to stop John. "We do not believe in this Jehovah God you talk about. We will kill you with *nahak*, if only we can get ahold of a piece of fruit or food that you have eaten."

Dear God, John silently pleaded, *please show these people that You are greater than Satan, whom they worship.*

Then aloud he said, "All right, you want a piece of fruit? That's easy." He walked over to where a woman stood with a handful of fruit resembling plums. "May I have some of these?" he asked.

The woman nodded yes. John selected three fruits and held them up. "Do you see these?" he asked the gathered islanders. He took a bite from each fruit, then handed one to each sacred man.

"You have seen me eat of this fruit and give it to the sacred men," John told the assembled people. "They claim they can kill me by *nahak*. I challenge them to do it, for I deny that they or their gods have any such power over me—or over anyone—by their sorcery." Then he sat down to observe their ceremony.

As the chiefs approached the sacred tree to perform their fearsome ritual, the islanders fled in terror. But John stayed where he was, watching as the magicians rolled up the fruit in leaves of the sacred tree until they resembled candles. Building a small fire, the sorcerers began to slowly burn the candle-shaped bundles, intermittently waving the smoking leaves around their heads and blowing on them to keep them burning. Now and then, they looked at John, as though they expected to see him fall down dead.

Like Elijah on Mount Carmel, John could not resist teasing the men who were trying to kill him. "Be quick! Stir up your gods to help you! I'm not dead yet; in fact, I'm perfectly well!"

Finally, the sorcerers said, "We will call all our sacred men together, and then we will kill Missi [their name for the missionary]. We will kill him within one week."

"Good! Good!" urged John. "I challenge all your priests together to kill me by *nahak*. If I come to your village in a week in good health, you will all admit that your gods have no power over me and that I am protected by the true and living God!"

Over the course of the next week, conch shells were blown daily to gather all the priests on the island to one place. Now and then, anxious messengers arrived at the mission house. "Missi, how is your health?" they asked.

"My health is very good; thank you."

"Are you not feeling sick? Maybe a little bit?"

"No, I feel fine. I hope you are feeling as well as I am."

When the week came to an end, John walked into the village, the very picture of health and vigor. Striding to the middle of the public ground of the village, he began to speak. "My love to you all, my friends," he began. "I have come again to talk to you about the Jehovah God and His worship."

He turned to the three sacred men. "Did you try to kill me by *nahak*?"

"Yes," they mumbled, embarrassed at their failure.

"And you failed, did you not?"

Reluctantly, the sacred men replied, "That's because you are a sacred man, too, and your God is stronger. He protected you from our gods."

"Yes. My God is the only living and true God, the only God that can hear or answer any prayer. If you will give heart and life to Him, He will hear and answer you too. Come. Sit down around me, and I will tell you about Him."

18

The Talking Box

as told to Jill Nogales

"I'm bored," I said, plopping down next to Ben on the hotel lobby's couch.

Ben looked up from his cell phone screen. "Me too. Everyone just wants to sit around and talk about grown-up stuff. I thought a family reunion would be more fun."

"Do you want to go walk around? Maybe we could check out the beach," I suggested.

My cousin Ben isn't the coolest kid around. And we pretty much have nothing in common. But I figured anything was better than sitting in a hotel lobby.

Ben nodded and grabbed his jacket. We checked with our parents and then walked toward the beach.

"Looks like the tide is going out," I said. "Maybe we can find some sand dollars."

We took off our shoes and walked on the wet sand. The waves tickled our bare feet.

"A while back, one of my friends found a twenty-dollar bill on the beach," Ben said. "He said it washed up on a wave and wrapped itself around his ankle."

I picked up a clamshell. "I guess you never know what you're going to find on the beach."

Ben stopped walking. "Hey, Kevin, what's that sound?" he asked.

I shrugged my shoulders. "The waves maybe or some seagulls?" I surmised. I mean, it's not like the beach is a quiet place.

"No, it sounds like an echo, but it's muffled," Ben responded. "Like someone talking underwater."

Then I heard it too. Ben and I rushed forward. We looked along the rocky shore and among the tide pools.

"It's coming from over there," Ben said, pointing.

We got down on our knees and dug at the sand with our hands. Together we uncovered a plastic box about the size of a shoebox. And it was talking to us.

Our eyes grew wide. Then Ben held his ear close to the box. "W-What do you think it's saying?"

"How should I know? I've never talked to a box before," I said, backing away.

Ben picked up a stick of driftwood and poked the box. "Let's flip it over. Maybe something's written on the other side."

It seemed like a good idea, but the other side was the same—plain blue plastic. The box was still talking.

"Um, maybe we should open it and see what's inside," I suggested at last.

"Yeah, OK, I'll do it," Ben offered.

I watched as he flipped the lid open and peered inside. "What's in there?" I asked breathlessly.

"Wow—check it out! There's a wallet, a set of keys, a Bible, and this." He held up a walkie-talkie. "The box must be waterproof because I think this still works. I can hear static."

Suddenly, a voice came from the walkie-talkie. "Hello, can anyone hear me?"

Ben looked at me and asked, "What should I say?"

"Well, say hello, I guess. And maybe find out who it is," I added.

Ben pushed the talk button. "Um, hello, this is Ben. Who are you?"

"All right!" the person responded. "I'm Josh, and I am superglad to hear your voice. Did you find the walkie-talkie with some other stuff in a blue box?"

Ben pushed the talk button again. "How did you know?"

"Because it's mine," Josh replied. "At least, it was until it got washed overboard in last night's storm. I've been searching the beaches all day, hoping it would float to shore."

"Where are you?" Ben asked. "We can try to get your stuff back to you."

"I'm south of Sunset Pier," Josh said. "Do you know where that is?"

I snapped my fingers. "I know exactly where that is! My dad and I took a walk on Sunset Pier this morning."

Ben handed the walkie-talkie to me. "What are you giving it to me for?" I asked, pushing Ben's hand away.

"Oh, come on. Just talk to him."

I took the walkie-talkie and pushed the talk button. "Hi, Josh. My name is Kevin," I said. "We're a little bit north of the pier. There's a sea lion statue on the pier. We'll meet you there, OK?"

"Yeah!" Josh said eagerly. Then the walkie-talkie went silent.

I picked up the box and put the walkie-talkie back inside.

Ben and I grinned at each other. This was way more fun than sitting in the hotel lobby!

As I carried the box of stuff toward the pier, I got to thinking about the wallet. Wallets usually have money in them. Not my wallet, unfortunately. But this one might. What if it had a lot of money in it, and that was why the kid on the walkie-talkie wanted it back so badly?

I'll admit I was tempted to look inside the wallet. Ben and I could split the money and ditch the box in a trash can. It's not like the kid would ever be able to find us.

But I knew it wouldn't be the right thing to do. It wouldn't be honest. And I was pretty sure I couldn't enjoy that kind of money.

When we got to the pier, we saw a kid standing next to the sea lion statue. He was holding a walkie-talkie.

"You're Josh, right?" I asked. "I'm Kevin and this is Ben. Here's your box."

"Oh, man, thanks a lot, you guys," Josh said, taking the box from me. "Last night when my dad and I went for a ride in our boat, a storm came up. I put the important stuff in this box; I figured it would be safe. But then a big wave washed it overboard." Josh opened the box. "I hoped the box would get washed up on shore. And I was hoping someone would hear me talking before the batteries went dead."

Ben nodded.

"The keys," I said. "Your dad will be happy to see those."

"Yeah," Josh agreed, "but that wasn't the most important thing in the box."

Here it comes, I thought. *It's the wallet and all the money inside of it.*

"The Bible is what you wanted back the most, isn't it?" said Ben.

Josh looked at his feet. "I always keep it with me. You probably don't understand, but it's really important to me."

"I get it," Ben responded.

Josh smiled.

We all stood there, looking at each other, and then Josh said, "Hey, thanks again for returning all this stuff to me. You guys are awesome."

As Ben and I walked back to the hotel, I couldn't stop thinking about how good it felt to choose honesty.

And I realized something else. I'd been wrong about Ben. He was actually a pretty amazing kid.

I decided that hanging out at a family reunion wasn't so boring after all.

19

Battle With the Devil

by Rachel Whitaker Cabose

Charles sat with his leg in a bucket of water. "Let me know when it gets too hot," a nurse said as she poured in water from a teakettle.

"That's enough!" Charles exclaimed when he could hardly stand the heat. Curls of steam wafted toward the boy's nose.

"I'll be back in a few minutes with more hot water," the nurse said as she bustled off.

Charles turned to his father, J. N. Andrews, who sat by his side. "I don't mind the hot part of the treatments so much. It's the cold part I dread."

After weeks of therapy for his crippled leg, he knew the routine: first, a long soak in a bucket of increasingly hot water, then a plunge into frigid water from the mineral spring that gushed out of the rocks near Our Home on the Hillside, a natural health center in Dansville, New York. Just the thought of the shocking cold made his scalp tingle.

"It will be worth it to have you running around again,"

Mr. Andrews said, setting aside his book.

"I know," Charles agreed. "I can already bend my leg better than before, so the treatments are helping." He wrinkled his nose. "I don't like having to eat whole-wheat bread and vegetables every day, though."

"I'll admit, Dr. Jackson's ideas about a nutritious diet were pretty hard to swallow at first," his father quipped. "But my stomach has felt so much better since we stopped eating red meat and started eating more fruits and vegetables. I wish I'd learned these health principles years ago!"

Unlike most doctors in the mid-1800s, Dr. James C. Jackson avoided poisonous drugs, such as arsenic and mercury, and instead treated diseases with healthful food, fresh air, rest, exercise, and water. Desperate for better health, J. N. Andrews had brought his whole family, including young Charles and his sister, Mary, to stay at Dr. Jackson's sanitarium.

"There's only one thing missing from Dr. Jackson's treatment program: prayer," Mr. Andrews noted. "While we wait for the nurse, let's ask the Lord again to heal you."

Charles bowed his head, grateful to have his father by his side. It was hard when he was gone for months at a time on evangelistic tours. Letters just weren't the same as his father's caring touch.

Charles left Our Home on the Hillside with a fully functional leg. He was thankful for the care he had received. During the next few years, he would wave farewell to his father many more times. But he never expected to say a much more permanent goodbye to another member of the family.

One winter day when Charles was about fifteen, his mother, Angeline, suffered a stroke that left her partially paralyzed. Her right arm was useless, and her words slurred when she spoke.

While their mother recuperated, Charles and Mary did extra chores around the house. Fortunately, Mr. Andrews was home to help too. He was busy revising his book about the history of the Sabbath, which showed how some Christians had changed the day of worship to Sunday. Every day he spent hours poring over old books, looking for details to include.

A few weeks later, the early spring sunshine streamed temptingly through the windows. "I'd like to go for a little walk," Mrs. Andrews said. "I feel stronger today, and it would be so good to get outside."

"That sounds like the perfect reason to take a break from my writing," Mr. Andrews said with a smile. He hurried to get his wife's coat, but as he helped her put it on, she suddenly collapsed, unconscious, to the floor.

Charles's mother never woke up. The next few days were a blur of tears, hugs, flowers, and a casket that held the broken pieces of his heart.

After the funeral, the house seemed dark and empty. Mr. Andrews decided to move the family to Lancaster, Massachusetts, so he could easily travel into Boston for his research.

In their new town, Charles and Mary settled into the routine of school. Their father tried his best to make their home cheerful, but he didn't have Mother's knack for cooking and decorating. Sometimes, late at night, Charles overheard his father's agonized prayers: "I miss my dear wife so much! She was the sunshine of our lives. O Lord, please be our strength and help in this time of grief."

Charles wished his faith could be as strong as his father's. Sometimes he didn't feel like talking with God at all. Hadn't they prayed for Mother many times after her stroke? Why hadn't God listened?

One day after school, Charles wandered idly into his

father's study. "What are you working on?" he asked.

Mr. Andrews held up a thick volume. "This book has fascinating information about early Sabbath keepers in Europe," he enthused. "You know, Charles, there have always been people who kept God's true Sabbath all throughout history."

Charles stifled a grin. A "fascinating" book to his father would bore most people to tears. He poked through the bookshelf, looking for something to read that wasn't too dry.

Suddenly, Charles heard heavy footsteps in the hall. He looked up, wondering who it could be. They weren't expecting a visitor.

Slowly, the door swung open, and Charles heard footsteps enter the room. Icy fingers of fear slid down his spine. He couldn't see anyone!

The unseen visitor pushed the door closed and marched across the room toward Mr. Andrews's chair. Frozen in place, Charles stared at the horrified expression on his father's face.

"Dear God, take the sight of him away from me!" Mr. Andrews cried out. He flailed his arms as if fighting off an invisible attacker. "Charles, pray for me!" he gasped.

In a daze, Charles dropped to his knees. "God, please save my father!" he prayed at the top of his voice, not daring to close his eyes. "Send the devil away from him. I pray this in Jesus' name!"

Mr. Andrews collapsed in his chair, breathing heavily. "Thank You, Lord," he murmured.

"Are you all right?" Charles rushed to his side. "What happened?"

"It was the devil, Charles. The Lord had impressed me that the devil would try to take my life to stop me from finishing this book. But, oh, the sight of him!" Mr. Andrews rubbed his eyes as if to wipe away the dreadful image.

"What–what did he look like?"

"A man came into the room dressed in gray. He was so tall he had to stoop to get through the door! He had piercing eyes and a hateful, angry expression. When I begged God to take the sight away from me, I could no longer see him, but I could feel his hands around my throat." Mr. Andrews shuddered as he gently touched his neck.

Charles gasped. "Father, your neck has red marks all over it!"

"I'm not surprised," his father replied soberly. "It's sore, and I feel weak all over. Truly, the Lord saved me. He must have a work left for me to do."

Charles nodded, speechless. He had never seen such dramatic spiritual warfare in his life!

"Thank you for your prayers, Charles," his father said. "God has a great work for you too. I'm sure of it."

Charles couldn't imagine what that work might be, but in less than two years, he would find out. In 1874, Charles, his father, and his sister moved to Switzerland as the first official Seventh-day Adventist missionaries to serve overseas. Together the three learned a new language, published magazines filled with Bible truth, and spread the Adventist message on a new continent. During his ten years of mission service, Charles lost both his sister and his father to tuberculosis. On a happier note, he gained a wife.

Through it all, Charles never forgot his frightening encounter with the forces of darkness. That moment had taught him to truly pray, not just to gain "answers," but to connect with the Source of life, love, power, and protection from evil.

This *Guide* story is compliments of the Ellen G. White Estate.

20

Hope

by Elfriede Volk

"I want to be baptized," Tila told her friend Brenda. "But not now. Not yet."

"Why not?"

"It is winter, and the river's icy."

Brenda laughed. She worked as an Adventist Frontier Missionary in a country where, until recently, believing in or talking about God was punishable by imprisonment or even death. So she was delighted with even the smallest advancement of the gospel.

But for Tila, getting baptized was a major step. When her husband had decided to be baptized a year earlier, she had opposed it vigorously. She had even threatened to leave him.

"You're crazy," she had hurled at him. "If you don't work Saturdays, you will lose your job, and with all the unemployment, you won't get another. What about me and our children? We'll starve!" But God had blessed, and they had managed.

"When do you want to be baptized?" Brenda asked Tila.

"In the spring, when the ice is gone. But I don't want to wait until then to start working for Jesus."

"You could help with our community projects and deliver ADRA [Adventist Development and Relief Agency] parcels to the very poorest children just before Christmas," Brenda suggested.

Tila was thrilled to hand out winter boots and good food at a home for the mentally disabled. But her greatest joy was bringing gift packages to the needy children in her neighborhood. When there were more children than packages, she bought gifts with her own hard-earned money.

Sometimes Tila invited Brenda to go with her when she delivered the packages. One home had two young boys and a little girl. Though there were no presents for the boys, everyone beamed when the girl opened hers and found a beautiful red coat with matching mittens. They fit perfectly.

"How did you know?" the mother asked with tears of gratitude running down her cheeks. "How did you know Anya needed a coat so badly?"

"No, no," Tila protested. "This isn't from us. It is from people in America."

"But we don't know anyone there."

"It is from strangers who want to do something to help others," Brenda said.

"It is a miracle that someone could care so much for a total stranger!" The woman shook her head.

Brenda was quiet as they walked home afterward. She had seen the poverty in Albania. She knew that the country was one of the poorest in Europe. She knew that there were virtually no opportunities for teens to get vocational training, much less jobs. Still, seeing the hopelessness in that home had touched her.

"I wish we would have had some presents for the boys too," she finally said. "That ten-year-old with the crutches—"

"You mean Gjoni?" Tila asked. "He is actually fourteen. He and his brother were born with thalassemia—a blood disorder that makes them weak and stunts their growth. Because they are sick so often, they don't really have friends."

"Are there no treatments?"

"None that they can afford."

Brenda sighed deeply. "Then we really need to pray for them."

Besides praying and asking the small group of believers to pray, Tila kept in contact with the family, making friends and telling them of God's love. She even asked them to come to her baptism in the spring. When she invited Gjoni to go to the Sabbath services with her, he readily agreed. His health had improved to the extent that, at times, he could walk all the way across town to the house where Brenda and her husband, Sean, lived. Because they had no church building, the small group met there.

Gjoni couldn't stop looking at one of Nathan Greene's pictures that hung on Brenda's wall. The picture showed Jesus as a shepherd rescuing a lamb that had fallen into thorns partway down a cliff. He urged his brother Thomi to come the next week so he could see it too.

"It is so different from the pictures in the Orthodox Church," he said. "You can see real love in Jesus' face."

"Can't," Thomi said. "I have something planned with my friends."

"Friends? Who, and what?"

"It is a secret group. But it has power, supernatural power. They want to tell me how I can get that power, too, and use it."

Gjoni didn't see any power, but he did see that Thomi was moodier and more irritable. He kept inviting Thomi to come with him on Saturdays, until finally he agreed. While the others were catching up on what had happened during the week, Thomi went over to the painting of the Shepherd and examined it closely.

"There's something written on the picture," he said. "See? Right here by the artist's name. But it is in another language. I wonder what it says."

"It says, 'He will take care of you. Stay close to the Shepherd,' " replied a teenage girl, who had taken English lessons from Brenda.

After this first visit, Thomi came quite regularly with his brother. Though both boys were shy, they learned to trust the group and even volunteered to read Bible passages. One day they were studying baptism, and Sean asked if there was anyone who wanted to be baptized. Both Gjoni and Thomi said they would like that–when the weather was warmer.

"Perfect," Sean said, delighted. "We'll plan for your baptism when Brenda and I get back from the States in the spring."

The boys' mother and grandfather weren't happy with the boys' decision. "Why do you want to get baptized again?" Grandpa asked. "You were baptized as babies. That should be enough."

"Yes," Gjoni agreed. "But that wasn't our decision."

"And who are these people? Where is their church?"

"They don't have a church. They just meet in Brenda and Sean's home."

"And you want to give up the Orthodox Church for that? Orthodoxy has been our country's religion for centuries. Communism couldn't destroy it. And now you want to give it up and follow the strange ideas of a foreigner? Give your heads a shake."

Health concerns delayed Sean and Brenda's return to Albania. In the meantime, Thomi quit meeting with the group and went back to his occult friends. Before long, Gjoni followed. Both avoided the church members and wouldn't return their messages. The group continued praying, and Tila tried to keep in touch.

Despite their illnesses, Gjoni and Thomi were fighters. They had to be to live with their pain and disabilities. But now they were locked in their toughest battle ever—the battle between good and evil. On the one hand, Jesus was calling them, but on the other, the demonic forces that had gained control through the occult would not let them go. The little group of believers redoubled their prayer efforts.

One Sabbath Tila arrived at Sean and Brenda's house beaming, with Gjoni beside her.

"I am now ready to be baptized," he told Brenda.

"Praise the Lord," she replied. They set the date for the following Sabbath.

But Satan refused to give up. Unable to get to the "sheep," he attacked the "shepherd." On Friday, the day before the intended baptism, Sean was hit with intense kidney pain and vomiting. Brenda called a few church members to pray. Several came over and, with tears streaming down their faces, pleaded with God to heal him. One ran to the pharmacy to get something for Sean's pain and vomiting. Another left and came back with a doctor and a nurse.

The ordeal lasted five days, with Sean's blood pressure climbing dangerously high. Finally, the kidney stone passed.

The next Sabbath the baptism took place. It had taken three years to reach this point. Gjoni was all smiles as his mother, little sister, and Thomi were there to witness the event. At the end, Sean and the little group of believers prayed that God would give Thomi the courage to take this important step too.

He did a few weeks later. The dark moods that had clouded his mind were gone, and as he renounced all spiritual ties with the occult, he felt completely free for the first time in his life. Besides Gjoni, his mother, and little sister, Grandpa also was there.

"I was against it at first," he admitted, "but Gjoni and Thomi have shown me from the Bible that Saturday is the right day of worship. But what changed my mind was the changes that I've seen in them. As I've told their mother, truly the Spirit of God is with these Saturday Christians."

That day Thomi had a special gift for Sean and Brenda—one that he had made himself. It was a beautiful drawing of Jesus wearing a crown of thorns. One church member was so impressed that he asked him to paint a mural with a Bible text on the wall of his home. But best of all, through their witness, the boys' mother asked for Bible studies.

Baptism was not the end of the brothers' spiritual journey. Both are active in sharing their faith with others, and Gjoni has brought at least twelve other people to Christ. Thomi is doing the same. Please pray for these young, enthusiastic Christians and for missionaries everywhere.

21

Stranger in the Big City

by Abigail Duman

The inner passages of the castle-like hotel seemed endless to sixteen-year-old Amy. Her trim, five-foot, two-inch frame felt incredibly small as she surveyed large ballrooms with shimmering chandeliers and square cathedral ceilings. A barrage of new scents, sounds, and people met her in the carpeted hallways as she wound her way through the labyrinth of rooms and passages sprawled out before her.

"What an adventure," she breathed.

The highlight of Amy's summer was Youth for Jesus, a program that prepared young people to reach communities with the gospel. After five weeks of evangelism training, including going door-to-door and giving Bible studies with a group of other teenagers, Amy felt weary and excited at the same time. She had pushed her sleep-deprived self to walk in Florida's muggy rain and brilliant sun. She felt homesick for her family in Vermont and sometimes lonely. But the energy left in her step and the sparkle in her eyes that bright day in August stemmed from her confidence in God's ever-present care.

For the final stage of their program, the Youth for Jesus team was expected to attend an Adventist layperson's conference in Orlando. Amy managed to secure a hotel room connected to the conference center and plucked up an independent spirit as she traveled through the hotel to the conference center for the first meeting that evening.

"It's a good thing I inherited a sense of direction," Amy said to herself as she wound her way around a cluster of tall men in suits conversing in the hallway. "And there's no rush to reach the meeting hall just yet, so I can take my time."

Amy amused herself for a few minutes as she looked in brightly lit gift shops through perfectly clear glass windows. A series of restaurants, frequented by hungry clients, also lined the hall. As heavy music beats roared from a nearby establishment, she softly hummed the tune of an old hymn to herself but quickened her steps when she saw that bottle after bottle of alcohol lined the walls of the shadowy area. Though it was early in the evening, nightlife in the hotel had already begun.

Suddenly, Amy realized that someone was walking beside her.

"Hi, Amy," a very tall man greeted her. "How are you?" The man looked to be in his seventies, with pure white hair and a kind smile.

"I'm doing well. How are you?" Amy replied. The man seemed very familiar to her, but try as she might, she couldn't place where she had seen or met him. *How strange,* she thought. *This man knows my name, but I don't believe we've met before.*

"How is your family doing?" the stranger asked.

Amy felt surprise wash over her when he seemed to be acquainted with all of Amy's brothers and sisters living back in the family's log home in Vermont. Unsure whether she should be comforted or alarmed, Amy stayed calm and continued walking in the direction of the main hall. Although taught by her parents to be distrustful of strangers, she valued his company as they maneuvered through the crowds of people. She felt safer to no longer be walking alone.

The two talked a few minutes longer until they arrived in the meeting area. "I'll see you around," he assured her as they parted ways.

During the next few days of the conference, Amy often found herself alone as she traveled to and from her hotel. Her friends from Youth for Jesus were off visiting with other people they hadn't seen in a while, and of course, her family was hundreds of miles away. Sometimes in search of something to eat, Amy found herself in a questionable area of town. *A sixteen-year-old girl probably shouldn't be walking here alone*, Amy realized each time.

Suddenly, the white-haired man would show up at her side; he walked with her from one destination to the next. A part of her felt very guarded toward the stranger. *How did he find me there on the street?* she wondered later on in the quiet of her hotel room. *How does he happen to be walking in the same direction as me?* But then she felt that she could trust him. Was this man her angel guard in the big city?

The conference drew to a close. As the last meeting ended and hundreds of Adventists swarmed the building and surrounding streets to prepare for departure, the tall man fell into step with Amy for the last time.

"I'm worried about making it to the airport in time," the teenager said, quickening her pace as she walked. "The last meeting lasted longer than I expected."

"Are you going to be all right?" the man asked.

"I think so." Amy nodded. "I'll do my best to get there in time."

"If you have any problems, or if you miss your flight, call me, and I'll help you," the man said. "If you need anything, just let me know."

"OK, thanks," Amy replied with a smile and a wave goodbye.

Amy stepped on the set of escalators in front of her when a thought suddenly crossed her mind. *Wait–what?* she exclaimed to herself. "*Call me, and I'll help you. If you need anything, just let me know.*" The words puzzled her. *I don't have this man's contact information. He never gave me his phone number, nor did he have mine. How am I supposed to tell him if something goes wrong or if I need help?*

She turned back to ask him what he meant, but there was no sign of the tall man with the white hair. He was gone.

Amy managed to reach the airport without hassle and boarded her flight home with a sigh of relief. *Thank You, God, for watching over me these past five weeks in Florida,* she prayed as she watched the landscape move beneath her airplane window.

After reuniting with her family, Amy described the kind man who so often fell into step with her in Orlando. "He was quite tall with beautiful white hair and a kind smile. Are you sure that he's a stranger to our family?"

Amy's mom shrugged. "I really can't say, but Adventist circles are small. I'm sure you'll meet him again and catch his name."

For year after year, as Adventist conferences and events came and went, Amy searched for the kind man in every crowd. *I wish I could thank him for reaching out to a naive sixteen-year-old who walked the streets of Orlando alone,* she mused, *for watching over me, and for being a friend when I had none around.*

Search as she might, she never saw the kind man again. But whenever she thought about his parting promise of help, she remembered two things: heaven is only a call away (no phone number needed!), and God's children never truly walk alone.

22

The Winner Is . . .

by Sharon Clark

"I won!" Jason yelled as he knocked off the last opponent in the Battleship game.

"Aw, you cheated," mumbled Greg.

"Chill time is over." Mrs. Conway rang the chimes to signal it was time for the class to return to their desks.

Greg sulked as he pulled out his science book. Mumbling under his breath, he continued to sputter and fume about the results of the game.

"I have a question." Mrs. Conway set the seventh-grade science book on her desk and waited briefly until all eyes were on her. "Why is winning important?"

Jason shot a quick glance at Greg and grinned. "I guess no one likes being a loser."

Greg scowled at Jason. "Especially if someone cheated."

Jason threw up his hands and was about to protest when Mrs. Conway interrupted. "I don't know if Jason cheated or not, but I hope he didn't." She raised her eyebrows at Jason and then continued. "No one wants to lose."

Turning toward the whiteboard, she picked up a marker. "Can you tell me about some important wars that were fought when losing could have changed the course of history?"

Cassie's hand shot up. When Mrs. Conway pointed at her, Cassie nodded vigorously. "We just studied about the American Revolution. Things would have been *way* different if we had lost that war."

Sylvia, feigning a British accent, responded, "You got that right, old chap!"

The class laughed and then quickly added several more items to Mrs. Conway's list.

"The Civil War."

"World War I."

"World War II."

"Can you imagine being under Hitler's rule?" Mark shuddered at the thought.

"Wars are often fought over land, but they're also fought over ideals." Mrs. Conway returned the marker to the tray and leaned against the whiteboard. "The idea of something very good versus something very bad is a strong factor in wars."

"Like World War II!" added Mark.

Mrs. Conway nodded. "Yes, World War II is a very important example. Hitler tried to convince his followers that his way would lead to a perfect world."

Greg shook his head. "Boy, did he have that wrong. And he really *did* cheat!"

"Yes, he did, Greg. He lied and deceived to get what he wanted. Thankfully, God intervened, and Hitler didn't accomplish his goal."

"Can you imagine everybody speaking German?" Sylvia shook her head.

"Can you imagine having everybody who was 'different' or you didn't like wiped out just because . . ." Jason struggled for the right word.

"Just because!" Greg finished his sentence.

Cassie frowned slightly. "Isn't that what Lucifer did in heaven? Didn't he lie and deceive to try to win against God?"

"Yeah," Jason nodded. "Isn't that what we studied about in the Bible?"

"Talk about a sore loser." Greg shook his head.

Mrs. Conway looked around the classroom. "So, what can we take away from this discussion?"

Mark groaned. "Lucifer, alias Satan, really *is* a sore loser. He's out to get us all if he can."

Mrs. Conway nodded. "Fortunately, this is one battle where we already know the ending, and Jesus didn't cheat to win."

Greg turned to Jason. "Sorry I accused you of cheating."

Jason shrugged his shoulders. "No sweat. I'm just glad we're on the winning side of this battle with Satan."